CONTROLLING COSTS
IN THE
FOODSERVICE INDUSTRY

Dorothy Pannell-Martin

CONTROLLING COSTS
IN THE
FOODSERVICE INDUSTRY

Dorothy Pannell-Martin
President, inTEAM Associates, Inc.

inTEAM Associates, Inc., P.O. Box 15237, Alexandria, VA 22309

Disclaimer

This publication is designed to provide accurate and authoritative information in regard to the subject matter covered. It is sold with the understanding that the publisher does not accept any liability with respect to use of the information herein.

Library of Congress Cataloging-in-Publication Data
Pannell-Martin, Dorothy
        Controlling costs in the foodservice industry/
        Dorothy Pannell-Martin.
            p. cm.
        Includes bibliography and index.
        ISBN-0-9666121-0-8
            1. Foodservice management. 2. Restaurant management
    TX911.3 -------1998.
    647.95068--dc21

Cover design: Suzanne Gore Reynolds
Editorial assistance: Gloria Johnson
Text design: Florene Love

Library of Congress Catalog Card Number: 98-93322

Printed in the United States of America

10 9 8 7 6 5 4 3 2 1

ISBN 0-9666121-0-8

Contents

Contents

Preface

Management in the foodservice industry is experiencing a need to control costs that is more intense than ever before. The author of this text recognizes the importance of a positive bottom line (profit) in all segments of the industry, whether the foodservice is a commercial restaurant or a noncommercial one located in a university/college, public school, business, or hospital. To be successful in today's world, management must be able to plan and control costs.

Controlling costs in the foodservice industry can be an exciting and challenging part of management, but financial success doesn't just happen. It requires management being knowledgeable about financial management, being flexible and creative, and being able to make changes quickly.

This text is divided into three major areas: (1) understanding and using basic accounting reports, (2) determining revenue and evaluating costs, and (3) using break-even point analyses and internal controls to ensure financial success.

College Credit

Persons who desire college credit in financial management and would like to supplement this text with further study may contact Penn State University about the Independent Learning program and course DSM337.

In the Independent Learning course this book will serve as the text along with the study guide by Dorothy Pannell- Martin, published by Penn State University.

The study guide provides examples of each subject addressed in this book with problems to solve and practice test questions.

Acronyms Used

Throughout this book, examples and information that will be of interest to a particular segment of the foodservice industry are identified with the following acronyms:

Business and industry = B&I
Universities and colleges = U&C
Correctional institutions = COR
Health cares = HC
Restaurants = RES
Schools = SCH
All across the industry = ALL

Glossary of Terms and Bibliography

A glossary of terms related to controlling costs appears near the end of the book. A bibliography listing all of the most recent resources used by this author in writing this text appears at the end of the book.

Acknowledgments

Many people have contributed to this book. I wish especially to thank my business partner and friend, Gertrude Applebaum, and my son, Stephen VanEgmond, Culinary Institute of America graduate and employee of the Peabody Hotel, who have spent endless hours helping me research the different food markets to determine how the financial control differs.

To update and broaden my knowledge of the different segments of the industry, I used a survey format. I express appreciation to the many who responded to my surveys in all segments of the industry. My thanks go to directors and managers who welcomed representatives from inTEAM Associates into their operations and spent hours answering our questions.

The National Restaurant Association, the Society for Foodservice Management, the American Society for Hospital Food Service Administrators, and the American School Food Service Association provided studies and publications on the different segments of the industry that were invaluable.

My thanks also go to Faisal A. Kaud, vice president, general services, University of Wisconsin Hospital and Clinics; Larry Appleton, former director of Martin Marietta foodservices and now an independent consultant, who provided me with much of the business and industry information; Fred Dollar, director emeritus, foodservices, Texas A&M University; and Gloria Johnson, Florene Love, and Suzanne Gore Reynolds for their contributions to editing, layout, and design.

I am extremely grateful to Penn State University assistant dean Sara Parks and the staff of the Penn State University Hotel and Restaurant Department for their encouragement to extend my ideas for controlling costs from the school market to the entire foodservice industry.

I gratefully acknowledge permission granted by authors and publishers for the use of illustrations, examples, and quotations throughout the text. I am particularly grateful to Paul McElvain, child nutrition director, Kentucky State Department of Education, who was responsible for my writing the *Cost Control Manual for the School Foodservice Director*, which I relied on heavily for ideas and concepts as I pulled together this text.

My special thanks and appreciation go to my husband for his patience and encouragement and for helping make time available for me to write, and to PEPCO, our cat, who spent the early and late hours right beside me.

Dorothy Pannell-Martin

About the Author

Dorothy "Dot" Pannell-Martin is president of inTEAM Associates, Incorporated. She is a former instructor at the University of Maryland and former director of foodservices for Fairfax County (Va.) Public Schools. Her foodservice experience includes assistant director for a Morrison Company's college account and employment at two resort restaurants. She is the winner of many industry awards, including Food Service Executive of the Year from the Restaurant Association of Metropolitan Washington, Most Distinguished Pacesetter Award from the National Roundtable for Women in Foodservices, Silver Plate from the International Food Manufacturers Association, Fame Award from the American School Food Service Association, and Eagle's Award for Outstanding Service to Schools from the Association of School Business Officials International and the ServiceMaster Company. Pannell-Martin is the author of several books and articles in the field. She and her business partner, Gertrude Applebaum, have developed the inTEAM Food System, a standardized approach to foodservice management that extends across the industry.

InTEAM Associates, Incorporated, is a foodservice consulting company that specializes in inTEAM Food System franchise training, as well as training in cost control and problem solving for foodservice operations in trouble financially.

1

INTRODUCTION TO CONTROLLING COSTS

CONTENTS

OBJECTIVES OF CHAPTER I

After studying this chapter, the reader should be able to:

- Appreciate the importance of controlling costs
- Identify the requirements for controlling costs
- Determine the type of accounting system in use
- Understand the differences between cash accounting, accrual accounting, and modified accrual accounting
- Explain the value of ratio comparison

IMPORTANCE OF CONTROLLING COSTS

Today, foodservice management's number one responsibility, even in the subsidized foodservice operations, is controlling costs. The foodservice industry continues to be made up of many small businesses with average unit sales under a half million dollars along with some giants in the industry. Consumers today are looking for good food and good service--and **value.** The greatest growth is among foodservices/restaurants that provide **value.**

In the past, some businesses/industries (B&I) and school districts subsidized the foodservice operation as a fringe benefit for employees or as a part of educating students--fewer and fewer such industries and schools exist today. This trend is enforcing the importance of controlling costs.

Cost control is the process whereby management plans and regulates costs and guards against overspending. A good foodservice cost accounting system will generate weekly operating reports that will provide management information on how the operation is doing financially. Understanding each report and knowing how to effectively use financial reports as management tools are critical to financial control. It is through this knowledge that cost control can be practiced.

Excessive costs are generally caused by (1) failure to operate by numbers and (2) operating with inefficiencies and waste. Seventy-five percent of the foodservice managers surveyed recently believes controlling costs will become a greater challenge than ever before in the next three to five years. Like many industries in this country, the foodservice industry has had to change the way it operates in order to reduce costs. **This is because costs are increasing at a faster rate than are revenues/sales.**

Operating as a Business

Business and industry (B&I) foodservices and institutional "nonprofit" operations, as well as all commercial foodservice operations, are expected to run like a business and meet the budget--and have a small to large profit. Most B&I foodservices break even or have seen their subsidies disappear or decrease annually. School foodservices that did not formerly have to pay for utilities are being billed for utilities and other "indirect" costs. Prisons are growing in numbers of people to serve, but foodservice budgets don't always keep up with the growth and in some cases are decreasing. Health cares, particularly hospitals, have seen great changes in their numbers and customer bases that have made downsizing staff and costs necessary. Small local restaurants have had to compete like never before with chain restaurants, especially fast-food restaurants.

Balancing Expenditures and Revenues/Sales

Balancing expenditures and revenues/sales has become more difficult because foodservice management has seen costs increase at a greater rate than revenue. Increasing the prices charged is the last resort, and year after year the industry has experienced increases in food and labor costs-- sometimes coupled with price increases (though usually not). As major chains have become bigger, and their buying power and controls greater, it has become harder for the self-operated restaurant, hospital, nursing home, university, or school to compete. There is no room for "sloppy" or "by the seat of the pants" management because there is little room for error.

Increasing revenue or sales will not always yield the profits that reducing costs will. On the other hand, having cost control measures in place will not guarantee a profit in a foodservice operation. Controlling costs cannot be done at headquarters. It is accomplished from the bottom up, through managers and staff at each cost center.

Comparing monthly financial reports with a realistic operating budget and established management goals will help to ensure that the goals for the year are met.

Changing Customer Base

A decline in customers has become an issue for some foodservice industry segments, e.g., hospitals, where "long-term" today means one week. Hospitals are downsizing staff and reducing costs in all areas as a result of decreases in patient days and employee customers in many hospitals.

Many businesses, institutional "nonprofit," as well as commercial operations, have cut back middle management and in many cases have suffered a loss in the clientele. As foodservice operators strive to meet their budgets or profit margins, they have raised prices charged, reduced service, and lost clientele. B&Is have encouraged employees to go outside to eat and have strived to eliminate on-site foodservices. Fast food restaurants have saturated the market, and some are losing ground; and customers are shopping around for the best value for the money.

The increase in college students living off campus is resulting in a declining university and college foodservice customer base. Fewer resident university students mean fewer foodservice customers.

This book is not a comprehensive text on operating foodservices; it is devoted to areas that comprise costs and are related to costs. It does not cover menu planning, purchasing, personnel management, food production, or marketing. There are many good texts that can be recommended that do cover these areas.

COST CONTROL--BASIC FUNCTION

Controlling costs is a basic function of management at all levels--not just at corporate offices. It is the process by which managers/directors regulate and direct the action of others to achieve the desired financial goals. Cost control should be used prior to assigning labor as well as before serving (by precosting menus and recipes), during service (by using portion control), and after service (by postcosting menus and making good use of leftovers).

Controlling costs and making profits are basic to survival. Management must have financial data to control costs. There are some basic requirements for anyone in charge of controlling costs in any organization or operation, as illustrated in Exhibit 1.1, such as knowing what costs are and should be, how to read financial reports, why costs are different, what can be done about the costs; and being willing to do something about problems.

Exhibit 1.1 Basic to Controlling Costs

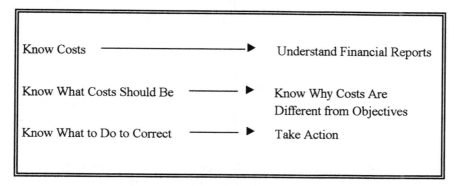

The six basic needs for managers in controlling costs in any organization or operation are:

1. Have a good, timely accounting system
2. Understand financial reports
3. Use standards for comparison
4. Be able to identify why costs are different
5. Know what to do about costs
6. Take corrective action

Each of these requirements is addressed on the following pages.

Good Accounting System

The "basic" requirement for managing finances is a good accounting system. Unfortunately, many of the small, privately owned and operated foodservices are without a good accounting system and do not have cost control measures in place. In other words, some are operating "by the seat of their pants."

Frequently, cost control problems result from late reporting. A manager should be able to view an analysis of each day's operation the following morning.

To control costs, the process of directing, regulating, and guiding the action of people is necessary to achieve management's ultimate goal of being profitable or being self-supporting. It is important to know what upper management's goals are for foodservices--corporate financial officers, company presidents, boards of trustees, school boards. Otherwise, foodservice managers may believe they are doing satisfactory jobs only to learn too late that upper management is not satisfied and is planning managerial changes.

When self-operated foodservices do not meet the business goals set, upper management or owners often turn to privatization as the answer. The basic question may be, "How much profit is desired?" The owner of a bagel shop may expect a 25% profit margin, but a school board would be delighted with a 2% profit.

A good accounting system is one that provides an **accurate, timely financial report that is understandable to management**. The financial report should detail income, operating expenses, profit margins, cash flow, assets, and liabilities. Cost accounting is a type of accounting that provides information in a format that is relevant to a manager's use in:

> Planning
> Controlling
> Evaluating performance
> Making decisions

Nearly every segment of the foodservice industry has developed accounting standards. Some of the accounting standards set are as follows:

- Universities and colleges--standards developed by the Association of Colleges and Universities, as well as the National Association of College and University Food Services
- Restaurants-- *Uniform System of Accounts for Restaurants*, 7th ed., by National Restaurant Association (1996) and American Institute of Certified Public Accountants (prior to 1973); the Financial Accounting Standards Board (since 1973)
- Health cares--uniform standards through the American Hospital Association and the American Society of Health Care Administrators
- Elementary and secondary schools--data kept and reported to the United States Department of Agriculture, influenced by the Association of School Business Officials' publications, and requirements of state departments of education

- Business and industry--standards recommended by the Society for Foodservice Management

Once an accounting standard has been adopted, it should be followed continually. There are some basic accounting principles that should be followed, such as:

1. Three reports maintained--balance sheet, income statement or profit and loss statement, and change in cash flow
2. Price paid when purchased--the value of the product or service
3. Each unit of operation considered a business entity and a cost center, having its own profit and loss statement
4. Expenses matched with the revenue for the same period of time

Management needs to know what is happening daily; however, most accounting systems are not designed to provide this information daily, weekly at best. The report should be accurate and in a format that is easily understood (not reams of paper that don't tell what is needed). An alert manager won't wait on the accounting system but will obtain daily accounting information. The point-of-sale (POS) reports, together with electronic time recording and computerized receiving reports, can be used to arrive at daily estimates of revenue and expenses. These reports can and should be available within two business days afterwards. If left to accountants, it can take 15 days or more.

Similar operations should be compared periodically in critical areas: (1) number of employees, (2) labor costs for each dollar of sales, (3) food and other costs for each dollar of sales, (4) overtime used, etc.--as discussed in detail in later chapters.

If managers have more than one unit they are responsible for, it is essential that financial data be broken out by unit with each unit treated as a cost center. If one unit provides food for other units, the costs should be established and prorated to all the units.

If the budget does not allow for an accountant, unit managers may have to prepare their own financial reports. Timely, accurate financial reports are essential!

Understanding Financial Reports

Managers must have a knowledge of basic accounting and be able to read and analyze the financial reports available. This means that managers must be able to read and understand a profit and loss statement, know some basic accounting terms, be able to spot trends, and know what to do to increase or decrease each figure. Management needs to train new supervisory staff and employees in the basics of finance. Brinker International and Pizza Hut have found training in finance improves their performance.

Analyzing the financial reports (see Exhibit 1.2) will show trends and uncover problems and errors. The bottom line is very important -- but what makes up that bottom line is what really tells management where costs are out of line. For example, the revenue is down in November and the food and labor costs were higher than in previous months or year-to-date.

Standards for Comparison

Management needs to compare wages and benefits paid employees, costs of specific food items, amounts of revenue being spent for food and labor, and costs of staffing with some other similar locations or with the industry standards. The profit in Exhibit 1.2 is excellent, but does it meet the expectations. This P&L would be more meaningful if some standards were available.

Means of Judging

There are a number of means that can be used to evaluate financial results. One or more of the following may be used.

- Internal standards of comparison, such as:
  - Budget (Exhibit 1.3)
  - Performance standards set
  - Prior periods
- Industry averages (Exhibit 1.4)
- Operations of similar size and type

Exhibit 1.4 provides industry averages as guidelines that show how similar and different the institutional "nonprofit" (or noncommercial) and business and industry (or commercial) foodservices are. If more is spent on labor, for example, less has to be spent on other costs in order to break even or make a profit. Unfortunately, many of the noncommercial, self-operated foodservice operations have labor costs that exceed 50 percent of the revenue.

Exhibit 1.2 Sample Profit and Loss (P&L) Statement or Income Statement for a Restaurant

Category	November Amount	% of Sales	December Amount	% of Sales	Year-to-Date	% of Sales
SALES: Food	$ 80,700	75%	$ 88,102	74%	$1,122,000	74%
Beverages	28,100	25	30,200	26	402,000	26
Total Sales	$ 108,800	100%	$118,302	100%	$1,524,000	100%
COST OF SALES: Food	26,631	33%	30,836	35%	359,040	32
Beverages	7,025	25	7,852	26	95,300	24
Total Cost of Sales	33,656	31	38,688	33	454,340	30
GROSS PROFIT	$ 75,144	69	$ 79,614	67	$1,069,660	70%
OTHER INCOME	644	0.6	644	0.5	7,728	0.5
TOTAL INCOME	$ 75,788	69.6%	$ 80,258	67.5	$1,077,328	70.5
CONTROLLABLE EXPENSES: Salaries and Wages	28,288	26.0%	$ 31,942	27.0%	$ 388,620	25.5%
Employee Benefits	5,222	4.8	5,442	4.6	71,628	4.7
Direct Operating Expenses	6,637	6.1	6,980	5.9	89,916	5.9
Music and Entertainment	1,088	1.0	1,420	1.2	16,764	1.1
Advertising, Marketing	1,632	1.5	2,129	1.8	28,956	1.9
Utilities	2,720	2.5	2,839	2.4	36,576	2.4
Administrative	5,549	5.1	5,915	5.0	79,248	5.2
Overhead Costs	1,323	1.4	1,646	1.4	21,336	1.4
Repairs and Maintenance	1,958	1.8	1,893	1.6	25,908	1.7
CONTROLLABLE EXPENSES	$53,094	48.8%	$ 58,560	49.5%	$ 737,616	48.4
Occupancy Costs Rent	6,658	6.1	6,658	4.4	79,896	5.2
Depreciation	2,849	2.9	2,849	1.8	33,948	2.2
Interest	2,876	2.6	2,876	2.4	34,512	2.3
NET INCOME BEFORE TAXES	$ 10,336	9.5%	$ 10,529	8.9%	$ 181,356	11.9%

Exhibit 1.3   Operating Statement Compared to Budget and the Variances

ABC Community Hospital
Patient Meal Service
Operating Statement
Period Ending January 31, 1998 (7 months)
Year to Date

DESCRIPTION	ACTUAL	BUDGET	VARIANCE	% VARIANCE
Salaries & Fringes Benefits	$531,224	$519,291	($11,933)	(2.3)
Food Costs	$358,673	$345,073	($13,600)	(3.9)
Supplies--Disposable	$ 44,712	$ 44,143	($569)	(1.3)
Supplies--China & Utensils	$ 14,363	$ 16,333	$1,970	12.1
Misc. Expenses	$ 980	$ 2,928	$1,948	66.5
TOTAL	$949,952	$927,768	($22,184)	(2.4)
Statistics				
Patient Days	72,112	72,500	388	0.5
Number of Meals Served	188,503	187,050	(1,453)	(0.8)
Number of Paid Hours	47,906	47,648	(258)	(0.5)
Number of FTEs	39.33	39.11	(0.22)	(0.6)
Meals per Patient Day	2.61	2.58	(0.03)	(1.2)
Cost/Meal				
Salaries & Fringe Benefits	$ 2.82	$ 2.78	($0.04)	(1.4)
Food	$ 1.90	$ 1.84	($0.06)	(3.3)
Supplies	$ 0.31	$ 0.32	$0.01	3.1
Misc.	$ 0.01	$ 0.02	$0.01	50.0
TOTAL	$ 5.04	$ 4.96	($0.08)	(1.6)
Productivity Indicator				
Meals per Paid Hour	3.93	3.93	0	0

Source: Faisal A. Kaud, University of Wisconsin Hospital and Clinics, Madison, March 1998.

Faisal A. Kaud of Wisconsin Hospital and Clinics, Madison, has analyzed the variances shown in Exhibit 1.3 and recommends the following corrective action.

Analysis of the Variance

Actual Patient Days x Budgeted Meals/Patient Days = Number of Meals Expected to Be Served
$$72,112 \times 2.58 = 186,049$$

Actual Meals Served – Meals Expected to Be Served = Excess Meals Served
$$188,503 - 186,049 = 2,454$$

Excess Meals Served x Actual Cost/Meal = Excess Meal Expenditure
$$2,454 \times \$5.04 = \$12,368$$

Add the Difference in Meals Cost Between the Budgeted Cost and Actual Meal Expenditure
$$186,049 \times \$0.08 = \$14,884$$

Summary of the Budget Variance (Over Budget)

Excess Meals Served	12,368
Cost Difference between Budget and Actual	14,884
Total $ Spent Over Budgeted Amount	$27,252

Managerial Action to Bring the Actual Operating Statement to Budget

- Review the reason(s) for serving 2,454 excess meals. Conduct daily audits of the service records including patient activity, status of admissions, discharge and transfer of patients, and frequency of diet changes.
- Identify and correct the reasons for increased costs of salaries and fringe benefits, food costs, and disposable supplies. Daily account for the labor expenditure as well as review the foodservice reports.

Source: Faisal A. Kaud, University of Wisconsin Hospital and Clinics, Madison. March 1998.

Exhibit 1.4   Sample Industry Averages for Comparison

Category	Institutional Foodservices	Restaurants and Other Foodservices
Labor costs, including fringe benefits	40-45%	30-39%
Food and supply costs	35-45%[1]	30-35%
Utilities, maintenance, custodial costs	8%	8%
Overhead costs	8%	12%
Depreciation	2%[2]	2%
Profit	0-2%	5-20%

Exhibit 1.5 provides some industry averages derived from surveys of foodservice operations in 1995 and 1996. A number of sources have been used for this data, and these are listed in the bibliography.

There are successful operations that spend more or less than these averages. For example, fast-food restaurants may operate with lower labor costs and an upper scale restaurant may operate with higher food costs. As long as the bottom line meets the goals of the owners or the board of directors, the exact percentage spent for each category doesn't matter.

The mix of sales will have a lot to do with the cost of food and/or labor. Restaurants or foodservices with a high breakfast trade will have higher labor costs but lower food costs for that meal, and if proportions are high enough, the mix will affect the percentages overall.

---

[1] These percentages will vary in accordance with management's goals.

[2] Institutional (or noncommercial) foodservices may not include a depreciation of equipment. Generally depreciation is considered an integral part of basic accounting, and most nongovernment entities do account for depreciation expenses.

Exhibit 1.5 Sample of Industry Averages

Category (1)	% of Revenue Spent for Food/ Beverage Supplies (2)	% of Revenue Spent on Labor Including Fringe Benefits (3)	Sales per Labor Hour (4)	Average Meals[1] per Labor Hour (5)
Fullservice Restaurant Average Check Over $10	31.7%	33.7%	$ 19.04	6.9
Fullservice Restaurant Average Check Under $10	33.4%	32.9%	$ 18.28	8.4
Fast-Food Restaurant	32.1%	27.1%	$ 20.82	
Commercial Cafeteria	32.0%	31.0%	$ 22.02	3.3
Hospital	45.7%	38.0%	$ 19.11	3.4
University/College	36.0%	42.4%	$ 15.67	7.9
Nursing Home	45.7%	38.0%	$ 11.88	2.7
School	40.0%	40.0%	$ 21.57	12.5
B&I	45-55%	37.0%	$ 21.00	5.6

Adapted from data from FoodService Director Productivity 1996 (published in September 15, by *FoodService Director)* **for the hospital, university/college, nursing home, school, and B&I segments and from surveys of the restaurant industry.**

Setting Goals

All foodservice operations should set goals--for how much will be spent for food and labor and the desired profit margin. The overall foodservice industry operations will become similar within the next ten years regarding how the revenue is spent as institutional "nonprofit" foodservices begin to operate more like commercial foodservices.

---

[1]Meals or transactions.

Why Costs Are Different

Knowing there is a financial problem and in what category of expenses is half of the battle. The next step is identifying why costs are different from were forecasted or budgeted. Management needs to be able to analyze the financial reports, make meaningful comparisons, and to identify why costs are different from the standards or budget.

If labor costs or food costs are out of line, "Why?" Is the reason justifiable? When the operating statement is compared with industry standards, it may be higher for a number of reasons; for example, labor costs are higher in some parts of the country than others--supply and demand, or unions, may cause the higher labor costs. Food costs may be higher also because of the physical location; e.g., lack of competition among vendors in the region. If costs are higher in one area, this may mean they have to be reduced in another. If the revenue and/or costs as shown in the monthly operating statement are different from budgeted and planned, there must be events taking place that were not planned. "What?"

Taking Corrective Action

Often when costs are out of line, it means a change in operation is needed. Excessive costs are telling management that corrective actions are needed. Knowing where corrective actions are needed is the first step. Taking corrective action may be the second step, and this may not be easy--but necessary to stay in business.

When managers of similar units have the opportunity to compare their costs and sales, they often solve many problems through an exchange of ideas. Colonial Cafeterias in Fort Worth, Texas, has used this means of correcting problems very successfully for years.

ACCOUNTING SYSTEMS

An accounting system is a set of interrelated financial reports that tell how well an operation is doing financially. It is more than a bookkeeping system, which just accounts for figures. It communicates financial-related information to management such as percentage of revenue spent in comparison with budget and with previous years' data. Management needs an accountant with a strong cost accounting background who will analyze figures in many different ways. Managers are finding they cannot wait for accountants and need to be qualified to obtain needed information and to analyze the reports produced. The financial reports should provide warning signs before costs become a problem.

Types of Accounting Systems

An accounting system serves many purposes, and the purpose will have a lot to do with the type of accounting system used. If the accounting reports are for management's use in planning, controlling costs, and making decisions and for long-range planning, a management accounting system is needed. If the reports are for stockholders, school boards, trustees, government, and other outside parties, a financial accounting report is needed. The emphases of these two reports are different.

With controlling cost, the management type accounting is needed, and this system is broken down further into three types of accounting systems:

- Cash
- Accrual
- Modified accrual

It is important to know which accounting system is being used. The Governmental Accounting Standards Board has defined the accounting system as the manner in which revenues, expenditures, and transfers are recorded in the official government system.

A **cash accounting system** records revenue when it is received and recorded and expenses when they are paid. An excellent example of a cash accounting system is a checkbook.

An **accrual accounting system** is one that recognizes revenue when it is earned, the value of inventory as an asset, and expenses when they are incurred. In an accrual system the revenue/sales and expenses are recorded when earned or expended and are carried in accounts receivable and accounts payable, respectively. Adjustments to the cash accounting system are needed in the accrual system in order to match expenses incurred with the revenue generated--over the same periods of time.

Exhibit 1.6 shows a comparison of a profit and loss statement on a cash basis and on an accrual basis. Note the financial balances and differences in revenue and expenditures between the two.

A **modified accrual accounting system** is one that recognizes revenues when they are collectible, and expenditures as liabilities when they are incurred. Most governmental funds, except enterprise funds, are accounted for on the modified accrual basis.

Exhibit I.6 Comparison of Accounting Systems

Category	Accrual Accounting		Cash Accounting	
	Dollars	% of Revenue	Dollars	% of Revenue
Revenue:				
Breakfast--Cash	$ 16,088	11.2	$16,088	13.2
Breakfast--Charge Card	3,895	2.8	3,895	3.2
Lunch--Cash	34,484	23.9	34,484	28.2
Lunch--Charge Card	11,492	8.0	11,492	9.4
Lunch--Invoiced	11,482	8.0	-0-	-0-
Happy Hour--Cash	12,600	8.7	12,600	10.3
Happy Hour--Charge Card	13,400	9.3	13,400	11.0
Dinner--Cash	12,589	8.7	12,589	10.3
Dinner--Charge Card	9,443	6.5	9,443	7.7
Dinner--Invoiced	8,943	6.2	-0-	-0-
Catering	7,058	4.9	7,058	5.8
Miscellaneous	2,657	1.8	1,050	.9
TOTAL REVENUE	144,097	100.0%	$122,099	100.0%
Expenditures:				
Food--Beginning Inventory	$12,608			
Food--Purchased	44,825		22,400	18.3%
Food--Ending Inventory	11,850			
Total Food Used[1]	$45,583	31.6%		
Beverages--Beginning Inventory	2,801			
Beverages--Purchased	8,645		4,200	3.4
Beverages--Ending Inventory	2,645	6.1%		
Total Beverage Used[2]	$ 8,801			
Total Food/Beverage Used	$54,384	37.7%	$26,600	21.7%
Payroll and Salaries:				
Management Salaries	$ 8,204	5.7%	4,102	3.4
Management Fringe Benefits	2,051	1.4	1,025	.8
Staff Employee Salaries	32,710	22.7	24,400	20.0
Staff Fringe Benefits	4,443	3.1	3,331	2.7
Total Cost of Labor	$47,408	32.9%	$32,858	26.9%
Operating Expenses:				
Disposables/Detergents	$ 1,881	1.3	$ 941	.8
Rent/Lease	7,990	5.4	-0-	-0-
Depreciation/Insurance	4,322	3.0	4,322	3.5
Corporate Overhead	2,882	2.1	2,402	2.0
Laundry	710	.5	400	.3
Music & Entertainment	1,979	1.4	940	.8
Advertising/Marketing	2,854	2.0	1,420	1.2
Utilities/Telephone	3,573	2.5	-0-	-0-
Interest Expense	634	.4	320	.3
Repairs/Maintenance	2,521	1.8	1,220	1.0
Administrative/General	4,200	2.9	2,100	1.7
Total Cost of Operating	$33,546	23.3	$14,065	11.6
TOTAL EXPENDITURES	$135,338	93.9%	$73,523	60.2%
Profit OR Loss	$8,759	6.1%	$48,576	39.8%
Less Taxes	1,974	1.4%	1,709	1.4%
Net Income or Net Loss	$6,785	4.7%	$46,867	38.4%

[1]Total food used appears only in accrual accounting column.

[2]Total beverages used appear only in accrual accounting column.

Foodservice operations that are expected to make a profit and adhere to good business practices should use an accrual accounting system. Using this, all revenues and expenses should be recorded, regardless of when they will be received or paid. Also, inventory is considered an asset. In many operations there are revenues received and expenses incurred periodically (even annually) that need to be prorated over a period of time (perhaps 12 months). Otherwise, these receipts and/or expenses distort the revenue and/or expenses for the month received. The value of equipment is usually considered an asset and the depreciation as an expense, but some institutional noncommercial foodservices do not consider the value of equipment as an asset or recognize depreciation as an expense. The health care industry, for example, does recognize equipment as an asset and depreciates it as an expense. Schools often do not.

Certainly management needs to know what the cash flow, or fund balance (profits from prior years), is at all times. With a cash accounting system, unpaid expenditures are not recorded until the close of the fiscal year. If management is not aware that a cash accounting system is used, managers may be led to believe their operations are doing better than they are doing.

Analyzing Data

To analyze data, one should first look at the profit or loss, sometimes referred to as the "bottom line." Is it a profit? How much? Or, is the figure a deficit or loss (shown in a parenthesis)? How much? Next, one should analyze the figures that make up the bottom line. The best way to analyze data is to focus on the percentages of costs to total revenue for each item. Finally, one should compare the two largest expenses, food and labor, for several months and/or a year for the same period of time (the seasons of the year may make a difference in some foodservice operations).

Together the food and labor costs should not exceed 65%-70% of the revenue, except perhaps in the nonprofit foodservice programs, e.g., school meal programs and nursing home operations where the costs of food and labor may exceed 80% of the revenue.

Using Percent or Ratio Analyses

Ratio analyses express the relationships between two items and may be expressed in several ways. A foodservice operation manager will find ratio percentages useful in analyzing the success of the operation. The percentages make a collection of figures more meaningful. For example, cost percentages allow one to compare costs for two or more periods of time and provide a means of comparing different-size operations.

It is important to evaluate the source of revenue--so trends (decreases and changes) do not catch one off guard. For instance, what percentage of the revenue is from breakfast? What percentage of the revenue is from the dinner meals? What do the other sources of revenue contribute? How do actual receipts compare to the budget? Do the expenditures fluctuate? Why? Trends can be spotted when comparing the revenue from month to month or from year to year. To determine the percentage of revenue for each item, the figure should be divided by the total revenue for the specific period of time (generally a month). Then the expenses by category should be evaluated in the same way, as shown in Exhibit 1.7.

Exhibit 1.7   Directions for Ratio Analyses of Revenue/Sales and Expenditures to Total Revenue/Sales

$$\frac{\text{Revenue by Source}}{\text{Total Revenue/Sales}} = \% \text{ of Total Revenue/Sales}$$

Revenue by Source ÷ Total Revenue or Sales = Percent of Revenue by Source
Example: Total Sales or Revenue for Month = $50,700 or 100% of Revenue
          Breakfast Sales for Month = $12,400 or 25% of the Revenue or Sales
          Catering Sales for Month = $10,200 or 20% of the Revenue or Sales

---

$$\frac{\text{Expenditures by Category}}{\text{Total Revenue/Sales}} = \% \text{ of Total Revenue/Sales}$$

Expenditures by Category ÷ Total Revenue = Percent of Revenue Spent
Example: Total Sales or Revenue for Month = $50,700
          Food Costs for Month = $20,400 or 40.3 % of Revenue Spent for Food
          Wages and Fringe Benefits = $19,450 or 39.4%of Revenue Spent for Labor

An example of converting dollars to percentages is provided in Exhibit 1.8. The revenue is thought of as being 100%--includes all the funds available. If an operation spends more than 100% of the revenue, the operation is in the "red" or has a <u>deficit</u> or a <u>loss</u>.

Another ratio analysis is comparison of the amount of inventory to the food costs per day to determine how many days of inventory and how many turnovers within a month. Two to three turnovers per month are common; however, with prime vendor service many foodservices are turning inventory 50 times per year at a minimum. Some health care operations, for example, carry between two to four days of inventory. This small inventory may not be feasible or cost-effective for small operations. This is discussed further in Chapter 5.

Other ratio analyses are used to determine productivity and can be found in Chapter 4.

A good accounting system will measure one very important part of an operation's success--financial success. It will not directly measure customer satisfaction or how healthy the food is. When comparing a restaurant's financial status, it helps to have a similar type operation; for example, compare a full-service restaurant with a restaurant with similar-size checks (amounts collected per customer). The 1996 Restaurant Industry Operations Report (National Restaurant Association and Deloitte & Touche) provides some average financial information (see Exhibit 1.9) that is helpful.

Exhibit 1.8   Percentage of Expenditures to Revenue/Sales

Total revenue/sales are $450,000 for year.

Payroll is $125,000, fringe benefits are $18,000.
Food and beverages used are $122,000.
Disposables, supplies, and detergents used are $14,500.
Utilities are $12,500, telephone is $2,400, maintenance is $560.
Lease/rent is $12,000.
Insurance is $2,400.
Advertising is $4,500.
Miscellaneous is $650.
Overhead (management or franchise fees) is $54,000.
What is the percentage of these expenditures to revenue?

Category	Dollar Amount	Percentage of Revenue
TOTAL SALES/REVENUE	$450,000	100%
Expenses	Explanation/Dollars	Percentage of Revenue
Labor	$125,000 + $18,000 = $143,000 $143,000 ÷ $450,000 =	31.8%
Food/Beverages	$122,000 ÷ 450,000 =	27.1%
Disposables/Supplies/ Detergent	$29,000 ÷ $450,000 =	6.4%
Utilities/Telephone/ Maintenance	$12,500 + 2,400 + $560 = $15,460 $15,460 ÷ $450,000 =	3.4%
Lease/Rent/Insurance	$24,000 + $4,800 = $28,800 $28,800 ÷ $450,000 =	6.4%
Advertising/Miscellaneous	$18,000 + $1,050 = $19,050 ÷ $450,000	4.3%
Overhead (Management Fee or Franchise Fee)	$54,000 ÷ $450,000 =	12.0%
TOTAL EXPENDITURES	$411,310	91.4%
PROFIT OR LOSS (Before Taxes)	$ 38,690	8.6%

Exhibit 1.9 Average Costs

	Fullservice Restaurant Under $10	Fullservice Restaurant Over $10	Fast Food
Food Sales	87.2%	76.5%	96.4%
Beverage Sales	12.8%	23.5%	3.6%
COSTS: Food and Beverages	31.7%	33.4%	32.1%
Salaries/Benefits	33.7%	32.9%	27.1%
Admin./Overhead Operating Costs	5.1%	6.0%	7.6%
Physical Plant/ Equipment	11.6%	11.9%	12.4%
Other	.8%	1.1%	1.1%
Income Before Taxes	5.2%	4.3%	9.0%

Source: Restaurant Industry Operations Report, 1997, National Restaurant Association and Deloitte & Touche LLP.

Terms and Acronyms

Some terms need to be defined or clarified before proceeding to other chapters.

1. "Revenue" is the sales or income expressed in dollars. "Revenue," "sales," and "income" mean the same thing and will be used interchangeably.

2. "Vending sales revenue" is the revenue derived from vending machines. Many foodservices include this as a part of general sales. When vending sales are 10% or less of the total sales, including in other sales is a personal choice; however, when they exceed 10%, vending sales should

be reported under a separate operating statement, whereby profitability of the activity is fully realized.

3. "Expenses" are costs or expenditures. "Expenses," "costs," and "expenditures" will be used interchangeably.

4. "P&L," or profit and loss statement, is often referred to as income statement.

5. "Interest expense" is the interest paid on money borrowed.

6. "Prime cost" is the total of food, beverage, payroll, and employee benefit costs.

7. "Profit margin," or "net profit," is the difference between the total revenue/sales and the total expenses--often referred to as the "bottom line" before income taxes are deducted.

8. "Gross profit" is the difference after the costs of goods (food) have been deducted. Gross profit is usually shown on restaurants' income statements or profit and loss statements (P&Ls); whereas hospitals, prisons, universities/colleges, and schools may or may not show gross profit on the P&L.

9. "Forecasting" generally refers to estimating the number of customers. Forecasting is a major step in controlling food costs, because the quantity of food ordered and prepared and the number of labor hours scheduled will be affected by the forecasted numbers.

10. "POS" is an acronym that stands for point of sale. It is frequently used in the foodservice industry when referring to a point-of-sale register or device (terminal).

A more complete list of definitions can be found in the Glossary of Terms that appears at the back of this book.

2
FINANCIAL REPORTS

CONTENTS

OBJECTIVES OF CHAPTER 2

After studying this chapter, the reader should be able to:

- Develop a meaningful budget and appreciate the value of a budget
- Analyze a budget and track it from month to month
- Interpret a profit and loss statement (an income statement)
- Analyze a profit and loss statement
- Spot trends when comparing profit and loss statements
- Understand the balance sheet and cash flow statement
- Identify the difference between controllable and noncontrollable costs
- Depreciate assets
- Identify the different methods of depreciating assets

Today there is increased emphasis on cost effectiveness and cost containment in every foodservice operation. A good accounting system that produces accurate financial reports is crucial to controlling costs. Financial reports need to be produced for the accounting cycle. The accounting cycle of most foodservice operations is monthly and annually (based on the calendar year). The public schools' budget year generally begins July 1, whereas others generally begin January 1.

Most foodservice operations own a large number of assets, which are depreciated throughout the assets' useful life. Some of the "nonprofit or noncommercial" foodservices do not depreciate equipment, or consider it an asset in their financial reporting system.

There are four financial documents, or reports, that this chapter will concentrate on: (1) annual budget broken down to a daily budget, (2) daily/weekly/monthly income statement, or profit and loss statement, (3) balance sheets, and (4) statement of cash flow. Also to be discussed are controllable and noncontrollable costs, depreciation of assets, and bank reconciliation.

BUDGET--DEVELOPMENT AND USE

A budget spells out management's ideals, or goals and objectives, in financial terms and is used by commercial and noncommercial foodservice operations. The budget is based on forecasted sales, estimated costs, and optimal conditions. It reduces somewhat the uncertainties in a foodservice operation and helps with decision making. Many restaurants, even chains, do not plan a budget, but when managers are introduced to budgets, they usually find them useful management tools.

For new management or a new foodservice operation, the initial budget is certainly more difficult than any of the succeeding budgets will be. It is difficult because there is no historical data to use when forecasting sales and costs.

The budget is a financial plan that projects the sales/revenue, and plans the expenditures over a specific period of time. Most businesses plan annual budgets; however that is not as easy for foodservices because sales may fluctuate. Foodservice operations of schools, health cares, and correctional institutions generally plan for a year but with the understanding that budget amendment will be made if the number of customers or clients served does not materialize. For example, if the budget projects sales of $50,000 per day and a 30 percent food cost of $15,000, and the sales are actually $55,000 per day, food costs will consume more dollars and the $15,000 will need to be amended.

In the past, some segments of foodservices have managed finances basically by operating within the budget (e.g., hospitals and nursing homes)--and have been accused of having the attitude of "spend it or lose it." Owners, school boards, company CEOs, etc., should feel an obligation to provide incentives to "underspend" the budget; e.g., some of the management companies operating nursing homes are rewarding with bonuses the directors/managers who end a year under budgeted expenditures. When bonuses are awarded to managers that end a year under budget, this tends to eliminate the attitude of "spend it or lose it."

Value of a Budget

Every foodservice operation needs a budget because management has two things in common, and they are a need for: (1) financial constraints and (2) a mission. The budget should be treated as a contract between management and foodservice managers to attain desired productivity standards and customer satisfaction.

The value of a budget is that it:

- Provides a written plan
- Establishes measurable goals and identifies performance standards
- Communicates the goals to others
- Acts as a controlling device
- Helps management foresee problems
- Acts as a yardstick for evaluating month-to-month financial data

Methods of Planning a Budget

There are three methods for planning a budget:

- "Baseline" budgeting assumes that all expenditures from last year were necessary and will be duplicated. The expenditures are increased based on how much the sales/revenues (or volume) are expected to increase. Using a baseline (last year's or last month's projected budget) can be dangerous if adjustments have not been noted. If last year's or last month's budget is incorrect--not reflecting actual revenues and expenditures--the errors will be duplicated, and in addition, other factors may have changed.

- "Zero-based" budgeting is a method of building a budget by starting from scratch and creating the budget by identifying, analyzing, and evaluating all functions before allocating funds. Zero-based requires starting with zero and figuring all expected sales and expenditures. Zero-based budgeting has some advantages because it requires creating each projection.

- A combination of baseline and zero-based budgeting is the recommended method of planning a budget.

"Flexible budgeting" is a term used to describe a budget that is adjusted during the year when sales increase or decrease, or fluctuations occur in many segments of the foodservice industry. In other words, the budget is not fixed. It is based on revenue and cost per unit of services, such as per meal or customer. Unless the amount of revenue and the number that will be served are preset, the director/manager will increase expenditures as revenues are increased.

"Top Down" or "Bottom Up"

The manager or director of foodservices needs to decide before planning a budget if there will be one overall budget or several unit budgets that make up the foodservice budget. The budget that is planned at the top for all of the units within the foodservices is known as a "top-down" budget and is frequently used. The decentralized approach, "bottom-up," has become popular in recent years as management at each level has been made responsible for the bottom line. For example, at Penn State University the foodservice director for dining services has a general, overall budget, that is made up of budgets planned by each of the unit managers. The Penn State foodservice director has made each unit manager responsible, not only for budget but also for marketing, merchandising, scheduling special events, promotions, team building, and in-house training.

"Bottom-up" budgeting is recommended because it places authority and responsibility at the level where the action (sales and expenditures) takes place. Many universities, colleges, and chain restaurants, as well as other segments of the industry, find that marketing, training, and other basics are best handled by the central office or headquarters, in coordination with the unit managers.

Factors to Consider When Planning a Budget

There are many factors to consider when planning a budget. Some are listed below.

- Historical data---e.g., from last year

- Economic indicators---e.g., low unemployment rate, new factory opening, major employer layoff of employees, or the payroll increases because of a negotiated labor contract

- Demographic changes---e.g., in hospitals doctors sending people home sooner; in colleges or schools, enrollment down; in business/industry (B&I), layoffs--all of these reducing the customer base

- Menu changes---e.g., restaurant adding breakfast buffets Monday through Friday, changing customer choice of food to low fat, e.g., fish and poultry

- Changes in operating procedures---e.g., decreasing on-site production units by centralizing preparation of all baking, salad preparation, and casserole/sauce type items

- Changes in funding/source of revenue---e.g., parent company where foodservice is located no longer subsidizing employees' foodservices

- Price changes---e.g., elimination of "an early bird" special, 5 percent price increase, entree no longer including salad and beverage but side dishes priced a la carte

- Changes in goals and plans---e.g., goals in past at a B&I operation being to break even, then changed to requiring a specific percentage of profits going back into the business or industry

- Market changes--e.g., decreasing income (fewer patients in a health care) while labor costs, food costs, and other expenses are increasing

- Weather conditions--e.g., impact of weather conditions on harvesting of crops, increased cost of cattle's feed, and the resulting cost of food--produce prices rising or meat costs going up

Steps to Planning a Budget

A crystal ball would certainly come in handy when beginning to plan a budget. No one can possibly know how the foodservice business will be from day to day, so how can management project with much accuracy the dollar sales? Initially, projections will be difficult and at best an educated guess. After several months (or several years) projections will be very close. Since most costs are variable, or semi-variable, and fluctuate from day to day and month to month, the accuracy of projecting these costs will depend on how accurate the sales projections are.

Questions to ask when planning a budget are as follows:

What changes in departmental responsibilities, functions, or factors will take place that will affect volume?

What procedures can management change, simplify, or eliminate this next year that could result in reducing labor hours?

Can management justify any additional positions proposed? Has volume increased? If not, why is additional labor needed? Will the additional labor result in increased revenue? Before adding administrative staff and/or office staff, did management do a desk audit to determine what each person is now doing? Is all the work necessary? Can any jobs be combined, simplified, eliminated, or computerized? What overlaps in work did management find? Are employees duplicating work--continuing the old way and adding the new way of doing the jobs? What equipment must be replaced? What new construction and renovations should be done?

Can management expect increases or decreases in customers this coming year? How will the customer base change?

There are basically four steps to planning a budget, and they are as follows:

Step 1. Project total sales.

- Use any former sales figures available.

- Project number of customers per day of week for each meal and arrive at total number of customers (covers or meals) at breakfast, lunch, and/or dinner.

HC
- Obtain projected patient days for the health care's next budget year, and project the number of meals served per patient day.

    Multiply the projected patient days by the number of meals served per patient day to arrive at a total number of meals per budgeted period.

RES
- Obtain calendars of events for restaurants, particularly those located in high tourist areas. Knowing the number and types of conventions in town can help management project sales and be prepared.

- Determine if any unusual occurrences may affect sales--weather conditions, special events, promotions--that thus may cause an increase or decrease in number of customers.

RES
- Estimate the average sales per customer (average revenue) for breakfast, lunch, and dinner; check average revenue per customer daily to see if the average (or better) is maintained. In hotel restaurants some groups of conventioneers are known as big spenders and others as low spenders, and this can affect that average check.

  The average sales per customer can be determined with accuracy if good sales reports are available from previous periods of time--broken out by meal. Divide the total sales by the number of customers to obtain the average sales per customer (average check).

- Multiply the projected number of customers by the average check amounts to project the sales for breakfast, lunch, and dinner.

- Add the projected sales for breakfast, lunch, and/or dinner to obtain projections for the period of time. Exhibit 2.1 illustrates projecting sales in a university setting.

The projections by day of the week for the year need to be as close to reality as possible; thus, keep sales figures by day of week and by meal for future use in projecting sales. Since volume will vary according to the day of the week, promotions can help those slow days---two for one, free dessert with purchase of full meal, etc.

Step 2.   Determine fixed costs.

Determine those costs that won't vary from day to day, e.g., lease of building or mortgage loan payment.

Step 3.   Determine the percentage of the total revenue spent.

Determine the percentage of revenue spent for food and supplies in the past; use previous records to arrive at these costs and revenues; divide the food and supply costs by the total revenue to obtain the percentage of the total revenue spent for food and supplies. Use previous years' cost of a meal/labor, food, supplies, and miscellaneous expenses, to project costs.

Exhibit 2.1   Example of Forecasted Meals at a University Dining Hall

Day of Week	Number in Period[1]	Average Number per Day			Total Number of Meals
		Breakfast	**Lunch**	**Dinner**	
Monday	53	220	780	420	1420
Tuesday	52	250	800	440	1490
Wednesday	52	255	830	440	1525
Thursday	52	255	820	450	1525
Friday	52	260	800	310	1370
Saturday	52	175	510	300	985
Sunday	52	155	320	290	765
Totals	365	1570	4860	2650	9080

Step 4.   Determine the differences.

Determine the difference in sales projected and revenue/sales and the difference in projected expenditures/costs. (Subtract the projected expenditures from the projected revenue/sales; if revenue is greater than expenditures, there is a profit; if revenue is less than total expenditures, there is a loss, or deficit.)

Analyzing and Adjusting the Completed Budget

The completed budget will provide guidelines for the year, which can be used for weekly analyzes. An in-depth monthly analysis can be done and compared with the budgeted revenue/sales and expenditures. It may be

---

[1]Period is one year. The numbers indicate the number of Mondays, Tuesdays, etc., within the year.

necessary to adjust the budget (increase it or decrease it). For example, the year's revenue is projected at $500,000, but at the end of the first quarter there is only $100,000 in revenue (not $125,000, which has been budgeted). The food and labor costs have to be adjusted. The health care and correctional institutions are more firm with the budget and may not be able to make adjustments (or need to).

To use the budget, break it into 12 parts--12 monthly budgets. If sales are evenly distributed over a year, divide the annual budget by 12. If the sales fluctuate from month to month, the annual budget should be adjusted accordingly. When the budget is broken down, the account is ready to be analyzed and compared--actual occurrences with projected figures.

Management is sometimes guilty of planning a budget only because it is expected or required by the boss. And once planned it is filed, and unfortunately, its value as a management tool is lost. The good manager and director will analyze each month's operation and compare it with the budget, using it to identify problems.

A typical income statement would have the current month's actual performance listed side by side with the appropriate monthly budget, and a variance column would highlight the differences between actual and budget (see Exhibit 1.3). Another report would list the current month's income statement (P&L) compared with former months.

First, compare the actual sales with the budgeted sales--higher actual sales than budgeted are desired, but drops in sales or failure to reach sales/revenue should be a concern. What is the reason for increases--is something working right? If yes, what? Or, what are the reasons for decreases? When sales have decreased, corrective action needs to be taken.

Second, compare the profit margin budgeted with actual profits. If the profits are down, why? Profits down could be due to a number of reasons, such as:

- Low sales

- Changes in selling prices

- Changes in menus causing food costs to be higher

- Increases in the prices paid for food

- Pay raises and/or increased costs of fringe benefits

- Lack of attention to forecasting, food production, and marketing

- Low food quality and overpricing of food items

Third, compare the revenues and expenditures of the budget with projected revenues and expenditures. To focus in on increases in expenditures, use percentage of costs to revenue or sales for analyzing and comparing the current month's data with the budget. Compare costs with some foodservice industry standards.

Don't adjust the budget unless the monthly review uncovers major errors. Such errors will need to be considered in the next budget year. Budgets are planned under optimal conditions, and deviations will probably be made under less ideal conditions.

Deviation Analysis

Deviation analysis, or variance analysis, is a means of judging what has occurred (actual expenditures with revenues) and comparing with what was projected. In deviation analysis the budget provides only part of the picture. The profit and loss, or income statement, completes the picture. With a computerized general ledger system it is simple to generate these needed reports within a few days of each month. Exhibit 2.2a provides an example of a school district's profit and loss statement where all revenues and expenses are compared to total revenue/sales. In Exhibit 2.2b, the year-to-date actual figures are compared to the budget. As can be seen in Exhibit 2.2a, the food and labor costs are within the guidelines, and there is a profit.

Exhibit 2.2a Example of a School District Profit and Loss Statement

DESCRIPTION (1)	SEPT. 1997 (2)	% (3)	OCT. 1997 (4)	% (5)	YTD (6)	% (7)
REVENUE:						
Cash Student Lunch	$10,122	28.2%	$11,985	29.3%	$22,107	28.8%
Reduced-Price Student Payment	23	0.1	55	0.1	78	0.1
Federal Reimbursement	17,710	49.4	21,532	52.6	39,242	51.1
Commodities	1,616	4.5	1,947	4.8	3,563	4.6
A la Carte Sales	2,418	6.7	3,173	7.7	5,591	7.3
State Reimbursement	671	1.8	672	1.6	1,343	1.7
Adult Lunch	1,865	5.2	119	0.3	1,984	2.6
Other	1,397	3.8	1,485	3.6	2,882	3.8
TOTAL REVENUE:	**$35,822**	**100.0%**	**$40,968**	**100.0%**	**$76,790**	**100.0%**
EXPENDITURES:						
Food Used	$13,487	37.6%	$16,695	40.8%	$30,182	39.3%
Paper Products and Supplies	1,329	3.7	2,062	5.0	3,391	4.4
Foodservice Employee Wages	12,483	34.8	12,416	30.3	24,899	32.4
Fringe Benefits	4,068	11.3	3,470	8.5	7,538	9.8
Maintenance/ Telephone	453	1.2	184	0.4	637	0.8
Indirect	2,602	7.2	4,989	12.2	7,591	9.9
Overhead	822	2.2	822	2.0	1,644	2.2
TOTAL EXPENDITURES:	**$35,244**	**98.0%**	**$40,638**	**99.2%**	**$75,882**	**98.8%**
PROFIT (LOSS)	**$ 578**	**2%**	**$ 330**	**0.8%**	**$ 908**	**1.2%**

Exhibit 2.2b   School District Year-to-Date Profit and Loss Compared to Budget

DESCRIPTION (1)	ACTUAL YEAR-TO-DATE (2)	BUDGET (3)	BUDGET VARIANCE (4)	PERCENTAGE VARIANCE (5)
REVENUE:				
Cash Student Lunch	$22,107	$23,212	($1,105)	(4.8%)
Reduced-Price Student Payment	78	74	4	5.4
Federal Reimbursement	17,710	38,457	785	2.0
Commodities	1,616	3,362	201	5.9
A la Carte Sales	2,418	5,785	(194)	(3.4)
State Reimbursement	671	1,325	18	1.4
Adult Lunch	1,865	2,010	(26)	(1.3)
Other	1,397	4,104	(1,222)	(8.3)
TOTAL REVENUE:	**$35,822**	**$78,329**	**($ 1,539)**	**(2.0%)**
EXPENDITURES:				
Food Used	$13,487	$29,765	$ 417	1.4%
Paper Products and Supplies	1,329	3,300	91	2.8
Foodservice Employee Wages	12,483	25,490	(591)	(2.3)
Fringe Benefits	4,068	7,832	(294)	(3.8)
Maintenance/ Telephone	453	600	37	6.2
Indirect	2,602	7,591	0	0.0
Overhead	822	1,800	(156)	(8.7)
TOTAL EXPENDITURES:	**$35,244**	**$76,378**	**($ 496)**	**(6.5%)**
PROFIT (LOSS)	**$ 578**	**$ 1,951**	**($ 1,043)**	**(53.5%)**

When the actual figures (P&L) in Exhibit 2-2b are compared with what was budgeted, it becomes obvious the school district's foodservice has not met projected revenue, indicating that participation (business) is falling off, and the food costs were over budget, thus the profit is below budgeted profits.

To calculate dollar deviation, subtract actual revenues/sales and expenditures from the budgeted amount. Management has to decide what is acceptable. To calculate percent deviation, divide dollar deviation by budgeted amount and multiply the answer by 100. See Exhibit 2.3 and apply the following formula:

Column C - Column B = Dollar Deviation (put $s in Column D)
Column D ÷ Column C x 100% = Percent Deviation

Ratio comparisons provide flags if the manager has good measuring standards (prior months when business was doing well, industry standards, and goals set). If the percentage of expenditures to sales is going up, this is a red flag. If the percentage is exactly on target, this is a yellow flag, which means management needs to begin to takes steps toward holding and/or reducing costs to avoid financial problems in the future. If the percentage is lower than the measuring standards, this is a green flag--keep going as you have been. Faisal A. Kaud of the University of Wisconsin Hospital and Clinics reviews the deviation in Exhibit 2.3 as follows:

Management Review

1. Investigate reasons for the decline in revenue of about 12%.

2. Evaluate reasons for not reducing FTEs to compensate for the decline in revenue.

3. Investigate reasons why operating expenses per transaction are over 12% higher than the budget.

4. Review menu and pricing. Compare pricing with the competition.

5. Review food quality and service.

Source: Faisal A. Kaud, University of Wisconsin Hospital and Clinics, Madison, March 1998.

Exhibit 2.3   Example of Operating Statement Compared to Budget for Seven Months of Operation
ABC Hospital Cafeteria
Operating Statement
Period Ending January 31, 1998 (7 Periods)

DESCRIPTION (a)	ACTUAL (b)	BUDGET ©	$ VARIANCE (d)	% VARIANCE (e)
Revenue	$1,592,430	$1,807,000	$214,570	11.9%
Operating Expenses				
Salaries & Benefits	$ 901,638	$900,728	$ (910)	(0.1)%
Meat/Fish/Poultry	201,453	221,083	19,630	8.9
Fresh Produce	59,566	65,333	5,767	8.8
Vegetables/Fruit/Juices	24,156	26,507	2,351	8.9
Canned Goods/Staples	177,680	186,667	8,987	4.8
Milk/Dairy Products	119,530	130,667	11,137	8.5
Bakery Products	86,544	95,305	8,761	9.2
Supplies Disposable/Cleaning	65,462	75,542	10,080	13.3
China/Silverware/Utensils	8,808	13,125	4,317	32.9
Minor Equipment	4,986	5,367	381	7.1
Depreciation	17,694	18,630	936	5.0
Misc. Expenses	41,495	19,853	(21,642)	(109.0)
Total Operating Expenses	$1,709,012	$1,758,807	$ 49,795	2.8%
Ratio of Expense/Revenue	107%	97%		
Net Income (Loss)	$ (116,582)	$ 48,193	$ (68,389)	(141.9)%
Statistics				
Transactions	287,862	332,169	44,307	13.3%
Paid Hours	67,862	69,840	1,978	2.8%
FTEs	55.7	57.3	2	2.8%

Exhibit 2.3   Example of Operating Statement Compared to Budget for Seven Months of Operation (continued)

DESCRIPTION (a)	ACTUAL (b)	BUDGET ©	$ VARIANCE (d)	% VARIANCE (e)
Operating Information				
Revenue/Transaction	$ 5.53	$ 5.44	$ (0.09)	(1.7)%
Operating Expense/Transaction	5.94	5.29	(0.65)	(12.3)
Net Income (Loss)/Transaction	(0.41)	0.15	0.56	373.3
Revenue/FTE	28,589	31,536	2,947	9.3
Operating Expense/FTE	30,682	30,695	13	0.0
Net Income (Loss)/FTE	$ (2,903)	$ 841	$ 3,744	445.2%
Productivity Indicators				
Transactions/Paid Hours	4.24	4.76	0.52	10.9%
or				
Transactions/FTE	5,168	5,797	629	10.9%
ANALYSIS OF VARIANCE				
Restatement of the Operating Statement (Actual)				
Revenue/Transaction	$ 5.53			
Operating Expense/Transaction ($5.53 x 0.97)	$ 5.36			
Net Income/Transaction	$ 0.17			
Transaction x Net Income ($287,862 x $0.17)	$ 48,937			
Net Loss	$ 116,582			
Restated Actual Loss	$ 165,519			

Source: Faisal A. Kaud, University of Wisconsin Hospital and Clinics, Madison, March 1998.

PROFIT AND LOSS (P&L) STATEMENT

The P&L (also referred to as the income statement) is the most useful of all the financial reports to management. It is an accumulative report that indicates how the operation has been doing financially over a period of time. Should it be done daily, weekly, monthly, or quarterly? The frequency of preparing it may depend on management's need for the results. If the foodservice operation is operating at a deficit or needs to increase profits, a daily P&L will help to accomplish the goal. (The P&L statement can be prepared manually, but it is easier with the computer and some of the popular spreadsheet software packages.)

Parts of the P&L

The P&L is made up of revenue, expenses, and net income (profit or loss), and is arrived at by using this simple formula:

$$\text{Revenue} \; - \; \text{Expenses} \; = \; \text{Profit or Loss}$$

The P&L is broken down into four main parts:

- Total sales or revenue--broken out in some detail, e.g., breakfast, lunch, dinner, lounge, catering, carry-out

- Costs of goods used/sold (variable costs)--fluctuate in direct relationship to volume of sales

  (The beginning inventory plus purchases made during the month less the dollar value of the ending inventory equals the cost of goods sold.)

- Costs of labor and overhead (fixed costs don't fluctuate with the ups and downs of sales--mortgage payment, insurance, management salaries, full-time staff, and fringe benefits)

- Bottom line (profit or loss)

Some labor may be identified as semi-variable costs. Many accountants and managers add a fifth part--gross profit (after costs of goods have been subtracted from total sales). The gross profits aren't really profits because fixed costs have not been paid--fixed costs may take a large portion of the dollar.

For the P&L to be truly meaningful, the sales/revenue must be for the same period of time as the expenses. Charged sales should be included with cash sales/revenue. The invoices for food, supplies, and other expenses, including wages for time that has been worked, should be increased as expense and those not already paid accrued in accounts payable. Accounts receivable are those revenues/sales not yet collected but earned, and accounts payable are those invoices not yet paid but owed.

In the P&L, the revenue should include the sales tax collected and the sales tax paid as an expense. Those foodservices receiving USDA-donated foods (e.g., primarily schools) should show the value of the foods received, and the food as used would show as an expense.

The operation's overall P&L comes first and then a breakdown into smaller cost centers or entities--e.g., by dining hall, by station, by brand, by type of service, and by catering (each separate cost center). It is easy for management to prepare a P&L daily with computers and a spreadsheet.

If a foodservice operation has a commissary, a warehouse, or several units, the cost would be broken down and charged to each cost center. Treat each site receiving food as a cost center and it will be easier to identify and correct financial problems. If the commissary provides food to other locations, the commissary should charge the units receiving the food for the costs of the finished food along with labor costs and other operating expenses, such as insurance, rent, supplies, etc., within the food costs. Every food operation, warehouse, and commissary should be a cost center and should operate as such. For example, the warehouse will receive its money for operating by adding a service charge or delivery charge to the price of merchandise delivered to each unit.

Each a Cost Center:

- Restaurant
  - Formal dining
  - Lounge
  - Catering
  - Coffee Shop
- School district
  - Each school
- College/university
  - Each dining hall
  - Convenience Store
  - Vending
  - Catering
  - Restaurant/snack shop
  - Warehouse
  - Commissary
- Hospital
  - Non-patient dining
  - Patient food
  - Snack bar

Prorating Operating Costs

The administrative costs, accounting services, and other costs should be prorated and charged monthly to each of the cost centers. Again, the ratio analysis will be used to prorate the costs. The operating, or overhead, costs should be prorated based on each cost center's share of this cost. The share is usually determined based on the amount of revenue each contributes toward the whole. See Exhibit 2.4, which shows the percentages derived by using the revenue. Ideally the costs would be the actual cost of services received or the cost of the finished product (food). The reason for using this basis of charging costs is that cost centers may sell products for different prices.

The total costs for the central operation would be multiplied by the percentage for each cost center to determine each center's share.

Exhibit 2.4 Example of Prorating Operating Costs/Overhead Based on Revenue/Sales of Each Unit

Cost Center[1]	Average Monthly Revenue	Percentage of the Total Revenue
Bethune Dining Hall	$ 87,045	16.1%
Brock Dining Hall	92,942	17.2
Diggs Grill	64,395	11.9
A-Z Convenience Store	80,290	14.8
Haley Dorm	95,438	17.6
Vending	49,900	9.2
Catering	71.562	13.2
TOTALS	$ 541,572	100.0%

Prime costs are made up of food and labor, which make up a large percentage of the total operating costs. The cost of food runs between 28% and 45% across the industry. The lowest food cost is usually in the restaurant segment; however, Outback Steak House restaurant runs a 39% food cost. Restaurants that have cocktail lounges often want to separate food costs from beverage costs. A better decision may be to consider each a cost center and run profit and loss statements on each.

Exhibit 2.5 provides a sample of a hospital's non-patient cafeteria that is operated like any other cafeteria and is considered a separate cost center. If this were a commercial cafeteria, the budget may not be a standard to reach because the company may not have a budget.

---

[1]Each is considered a "cost center" because each has revenue/sales and expenses; the warehouse is treated as a cost center and obtains revenue from a charge placed on every case of food/supplies delivered.

Exhibit 2.5 Sample Cafeteria P&L Statement Compared to Budget

Category (1)	January (2)	% of Total Revenue (3)	February (4)	% of Total Revenue (5)	Year-to-Date (6)	% of Total Revenue (7)	Budget (8)	% of Variance (9)
REVENUE/SALES:								
Breakfast (7:30-10:00 a.m.)								
Cash	$ 3,846	4.8%	$ 3,102	4.4%	$ 6,948	4.7%	$ 7,940	(12.5)
Prepaid Meals	2,480	3.2	2,188	3.1	4,668	3.2	4,502	3.7
Total Breakfast Sales	$ 6,326	8.1	$ 5,290	7.5	$ 11,616	7.9%	$ 12,442	(6.6)
Lunch (10:00 a.m.-2:00 p.m.)								
Cash	$ 25,190	32.3	$ 23,120	33.0	$ 48,310	32.7%	$ 47,958	7.3
Prepaid Meals	9,300	12.0	8,902	12.7	18.,202	12.3	17,990	1.3
Total Lunch Sales	$ 34,490	44.3	$ 32,022	45.7	$ 66,512	45.0%	$ 65,948	8.6
Dinner (5:00-8:00 p.m.)								
Cash	$ 13,950	17.9	$ 13,015	18.6	$ 26,965	18.2%	$ 27,100	(.5)
Prepaid Meals	4,650	6.0	4,201	6.0	8,851	6.0	8,200	7.9
Total Dinner Sales	$ 18,600	23.9	$ 17,216	24.6%	$ 35,816	24.2%	$ 35,300	1.5
Vending Sales	$ 6,206	8.0	$ 5,290	7.6	$ 11,496	7.8%	$ 10,290	11.7
Catering	3,450		3,055		6,505	4.4	7,010	(7.2)
Gift Shop	6,740		6,040		12,780	8.6	12,200	4.8
Other Revenue	2,020		1,090		3,110	2.1	2,900	7.2
TOTAL SALES[1]	$ 77,832	100.0%	$ 70,003	100.0%	$ 147,835	100.0%	$146,090	1.2
EXPENDITURES:								
Food and Beverage Used								
Beginning Inventory	$ 5,272		$ 5,010		$ 10,282			
+ Food Purchased	+ 26,970		+25,091		52,061			
− Ending Inventory =	− 5,010		− 4,900		9,910			
Total Costs of Food Used	$ 27,232	35.0%	$ 25,201	36.0%	$ 52,433	35.5%	$ 51,130	2.6
Gross Profits[2]	$ 50,600	65.0%	$ 44,802	64.0%	$ 95,402	64.5%	$ 94,960	.5
Labor Costs[3]								
Salaries--Full-Time								
Employees	$ 18,571	23.9%	$ 17,249	24.6	$ 35,820		$ 35,820	- 0 -
Fringe Benefits	+ 6,335	8.1	5,852	8.4	12,187		12,187	- 0 -
Substitute/Part-Time								
Employees	+ 3,891	5.0	3,500	5.0	7,391		6,900	7.1
Total Labor Costs	$ 28,797	37.0%	$ 26,601	38	$ 55,398	37.5%	$ 54,907	.9

[1]Revenue/sales include accounts receivable.

[2]Gross profits are revenue left after cost of goods sold has been deducted. This may or may not appear in the P&L.

[3]The central administration or headquarters staff salaries and fringe benefits are not included here but under administrative costs.

Exhibit 2.5   Sample Cafeteria P&L Statement Compared to Budget (continued)

Category (1)	January (2)	% of Total Revenue (3)	February (4)	% of Total Revenue (5)	Year-to-Date (6)	% of Total Revenue (7)	Budget (8)	% of Variance (9)
Other Operating Cost:								
Supply/Detergent	$ 2,334	3.0%	$ 2,070	3.0%	$ 4,404	3.0%	$ 4,000	10.1
Small Equipment	546	.7	320	.5	866	.6	800	8.3
Utilities	934	1.2	860	1.1	1,794	1.2	1,800	(.3)
Telephone	308	.4	290	.4	598	.4	600	- 0 -
Marketing/Promotion	1,500	1.9	1,000	1.4	2,500	1.7	3,000	(16.7)
Maintenance	1,557	2.0	689	1.0	2,246	1.5	2,000	12.3
Indirect	750	1.0	700	1.0	1,450	1.0	2,000	27.5
Administrative	7,333	9.4	7,333	10.5	14,666	10.0	14,666	- 0 -
Overhead	2,101	2.3	1,159	1.7	3,260	2.2	3,224	1.1
Total Operating Costs:	$ 17,363	21.9%	$ 14,421	20.6%	$ 31,284	21.5%	$ 32,090	(2.5)
Depreciation	1,790	2.8%	1,790	2.6%	3,580	2.4%	3,580	- 0 -
Total Expenditures	$ 75,182	96.7%	$ 68,013	97.2%	$143,195	96.9%	$141,707	1.1
PROFIT OR LOSS BEFORE TAXES	$ 2,650	3.3%	$ 1,990	2.8%	$ 4,640	3.1%	$4,383	(5.9)

In the above exhibit, the year-to-date data is compared with the budget projections and the differences are, for example: $6,948 cash revenue (year-to-date) compared to budget of $7,940 equals $992 less than budgeted.

These differences are shown as variances, as follows:

$ - 992 ÷ $7,940 = (.1249) or (12.5%) variance
To convert the decimal point of (.1249) to (12.5%) multiply by 100.

The costs in a hospital foodservice need to be broken out and assigned to patient and non-patient meals. This can be done by determining what percentage of the meals belong to each. Then the department's expenses, e.g., food, labor, supplies, and other costs, can be divided accordingly. Prescribed nourishments may need to be treated separately. The nourishments are often an expensive area, and an accurate accounting method is needed to capture the costs.

A restaurant manager may need to separate the expenses and revenue for catering, a cocktail lounge, a carry-out section, and sit-down service to see what each contributes to the whole.

---

1 Accounts payable are included in the costs

Steps to Analyzing the P&L

Compare and analyze P&Ls vertically and horizontally with a minimum of two different months or years.

- Look at the bottom-line dollars. Does the foodservice operation have a profit or loss? The deficit or loss is shown with ( ) around the figure.

- Look at total dollars in revenue. Is the revenue up or down? How much?

- What percent of the total revenue does each category contribute?

- Is the revenue up in February? Is the revenue down? Why? February is a short month and may need to be broken down to number of days of service to determine if February's revenue is down.

- Compare percentages of revenue spent for food costs. Percentages should not fluctuate from month to month. If they have, why? Could an inaccurate inventory affect the food cost percentage? Could an electrical storm have caused the large freezer to thaw and cause food loss and increased food costs? The reasons become important--to avoid repeating.

- What percent of the revenue is spent on full-time labor? On fringe benefits? What percent of the revenue is spent on part-time labor/substitutes? Do these costs of part-time employees fluctuate from one month to the other? If so, why? If employees were paid for days when there was no revenue, the percentage of revenue spent on labor would be greater in the months with paid holidays and vacations.

- How much is being spent on maintenance, utilities, etc.?

- What percent of the revenue/sales is spent for overhead and administrative costs? Do overhead and administrative costs exceed 10%? If the costs do exceed 10%, take an in-depth look at the costs.

- What percent of the revenue is left for profit? Does this meet goals or expectations?

The foodservice industry standards can be used for comparing--as well as prior years' records. Some segments of the foodservice industry run higher labor costs and/or food costs than others. For example, hospitals, schools, and business and industry foodservice operations have done so in the past. This is changing as budgets are becoming tighter.

Self-operated B&Is tend to run higher labor costs than do contracted ones--thus it is evident that the costs can be decreased by the self-operated B&I if the goals or constraints have been set. Many self-operated B&Is are making rapid changes, and the high labor coats are on the decline as self-operated management has learned that upper management's goals have changed. Exhibit 2.6 provides an example. Note that though the profit and loss statement is for August, it shows the previous month's data for comparison purposes.

The P&L statement should contain the relevant budget information. In the business world, a budget is an essential tool of management and is a major part of the strategic plan of the enterprise. Without a budget to evaluate the enterprise's performance, an organization is navigating in the dark.

Exhibit 2.6   Contracted Electric Company Foodservice P&L for August

REVENUE	June ($)	% of Revenue	July ($)	% of Revenue	August ($)	% of Revenue	Year-to-Date ($)	% of Revenue
Convenience Store	$ 37,841	77.8%	$ 37,392	76.0%	$ 41,255	79.2%	$ 310,635	77.7%
Catering	$ 2,043	4.2%	$ 1,919	3.9%	$ 2,240	4.3%	$ 16,539	4.1%
Vending/ Cafeteria	$ 1,313	2.7%	$ 1,378	2.8%	$ 1,510	2.9%	$ 11,203	2.8%
Management/ Executive Dining	$ 7,442	15.3%	$ 8,511	17.3%	$ 7,085	13.6%	$ 61,435	15.4%
TOTAL REVENUE/ SALES	$ 48,639	100.0%	$ 49,200	100.0%	$ 52,090	100.0%	$399,812	100.0%
EXPENSES								
Variable Costs: Food/ Beverages	$ 18,180	37.4%	$ 18,155	36.9%	$ 18,804	36.1%	$143,932	36.0%
Disposables/ Supplies	$ 2,431	5.0%	$ 2,500	4.8%	$ 2,396	4.6%	$ 17,192	4.3%
Part-Time Labor	$ 9,591	19.7%	$ 9,250	18.8%	$ 9,845	18.9%	$ 62,770	15.7%
Employer Tax on Part-Time Employees	$ 815	1.7%	$ 786	1.6%	$ 837	1.6%	$ 5,335	1.3%
Management Fee (4.7% of Sales)	$ 2,286	4.7%	$ 2,312	4.7%	$ 2,448	4.7%	$ 18,791	4.7%
Total Variable Costs	$ 33,303	68.5%	$ 33,003	66.8%	$ 34,330	65.9%	$248,020	62%

Exhibit 2.6   Contracted Electric Company Foodservice
P&L for August (continued)

REVENUE	June $	% of Revenue	July $	% of Revenue	August $	% of Revenue	Year-to-Date $	% of Revenue
Overhead Costs (or Fixed Costs):								
Salaries/Wages	$6,250	12.9%	$6,250	12.7%	$6,250	12.0%	$50,000	12.5%
Employee Benefits	$2,918	6.0%	$2,918	5.9%	$2,918	5.6%	$23,344	5.8%
Administrative Costs	$3,891	8.0%	$3,891	7.9%	$3,891	7.5%	$31,128	7.8%
Lease/Rent	-0-	-0-	-0-	-0-	-0-	-0-	-0-	-0-
Insurance	80	.2%	80	.2%	80	.2%	640	.2%
Loan Payment	$325	.7%	$325	.7%	$325	.6%	$2,600	.6%
Music/ Entertainment	$290	.6%	$290	.6%	$290	.6%	$2,320	.5%
Utilities	$261	.5%	$261	.5%	$261	.5%	$2,088	.5%
Maintenance	$890	1.8%	$890	1.8%	$890	1.7%	$7,120	1.8%
Depreciation	$1,430	2.9%	$1,430	2.9%	$1,430	2.7%	$11,440	2.9%
Total Overhead Costs	$16,335	33.6%	$16,335	33.2%	$16,335	31.4%	$130,580	32.6%
TOTAL EXPENSES	$49,638	102.1%	$49,338	100.3%	$50,665	97.3%	$378,600	94.7%
Company Liaison Manager	$200	.4%	$200	.4%	$200	.4%	$1600	.4%
PROFIT/LOSS BEFORE TAX	$(1,199)	(2.5%)	$(338)	(.7%)	$1,225	2.3%	$19,612	4.9%

Analysis of the P&L in Exhibit 2.6 is as follows:

● Looking at the bottom line, August is much improved over June and July, and there is a profit year-to-date. What are the goals? Does this meet goals set? If it is $30,000 for the year, the goal is obtainable.

- Revenue is up at the convenience store in August. A larger percentage of the total revenue is from the convenience store's sales.

- Catering is up from June and July.

- Vending and cafeteria sales are up slightly.

- Executive dining is down considerably. Maybe this is due to vacations or meetings outside of headquarters.

- Overall the sales are up for August.

- Food costs are down in August (percentage of revenue is 36.1%), though the dollars are up slightly.

- Disposable costs are down.

- Part-time labor is up slightly in dollars but percentage-wise it is lower than June and July.

- The total variable costs are higher over the summer months than in prior months (62% year-to-date, compared to 68.5%, 66.8%, 65.9%). If the company's goals are to keep variable costs at 60% or lower, the summer months are in trouble. This affects the profit margin. If the variable cost is 65.9%, the contribution margin is 34.1%. That is the amount available to pay fixed costs and for a profit over the fixed costs paid is below expectations.

- The fixed costs are not consuming as much of the revenue because sales are up.

- If the sales remain high the rest of the year, this company's foodservice will exceed the goals of $30,000.

BALANCE SHEET

The balance sheet provides a "snapshot" of how the company or operation is doing on a specific day; it freezes the action. It is called a balance sheet because the assets equal liabilities plus owner's equity. It is a financial report that provides the financial condition of the operation at that point in time. It shows the assets and how they balance against liabilities. It tells the operation's worth--which includes actual cash on hand, accounts receivable, and the value of inventory and supplies. Thus, the balance sheet is not as much a management tool to a manager as is the P&L or income statement. The balance sheet is made up of--

Assets   =   Liabilities + Owners' Equities

The balance sheet does not tell the profitability or cash flow, but it does tell the company's worth.

Assets

The assets are generally divided into three or more categories: current, fixed, and other. The current assets will list the most fluid assets first--e.g., cash, followed by accounts receivable, inventory, dishes and silver, prepaid expenses.

The fixed assets include the more permanent items first--e.g., land, followed by buildings, large equipment, furniture, less depreciation on all. Depreciation is discussed later in this chapter.

Liabilities

Liabilities are often divided into two categories: current and long-term. The current liabilities are those that will be paid off within the year. The long-term liabilities are those that will go on for years, e.g., mortgage payments.

Owner's Equity or Fund Balance

For the commercial foodservice operation the owner's equity is the money invested by the owners and its accumulated earnings. In the case of a nonprofit foodservice, the fund balance is the accumulative revenue beyond the costs in previous years. Thus this section of the balance sheet represents the investment and earnings left over after commitments are met--the difference between the assets and the liabilities. With the profit-oriented operation, this may belong to the stockholders. In a nonprofit operation, it is often referred to as fund balance. For example, the schools that operate under the National Child Nutrition Programs are restricted to a fund balance not to exceed three months of operating costs.

An example of a balance sheet for a commercial restaurant is provided in Exhibit 2.7. By having two or more years side by side, one can compare how the operation is doing. Assets have increased, but the question may be, is that increase sufficient for management?

Exhibit 2.7   Example of Balance Sheet for Kristie's Restaurant

SOURCE	1997	1996
Current assets		
Cash	$ 65,200	$ 37,400
Accounts receivable	35,300	31,500
Inventory		
Food & beverages	8,200	9,320
Disposables/supplies	6,100	5,200
Total current assets	$ 114,800	$ 83,420
Fixed assets		
Furniture & equipment	$ 136,700	$136,700
Less depreciation	60,200	30,100
Total fixed assets	$ 76,500	$106,800
TOTAL ASSETS	$ 191,300	$190,220
Current liabilities		
Accounts payable	$ 42,600	$ 44,300
Wages payable	8,340	8,250
Sales tax payable	2,300	2,600
Long-term liabilities		
Long-term loan	56,060	62,040
TOTAL LIABILITIES	$109,300	$ 117,190
Owner's Equity	$ 82,000	$ 73,030
TOTAL LIABILITIES AND OWNER'S EQUITY	$ 191,300	$ 190,220

CASH FLOW STATEMENT

The cash flow statement, often referred to as the statement of change, shows the cash inflow and outflow for a period of time. The cash includes revenue from cash sales, collection of accounts receivable, bank loans, depreciation allowance, and cash put in by the owners. The expenditures are made up of labor costs, food costs, purchase of equipment, lease, insurance, utilities, and miscellaneous other costs.

CONTROLLABLE AND NONCONTROLLABLE COSTS

Costs may be divided into categories of fixed costs, variable costs, controllable costs, and noncontrollable costs. Controllable costs, like variable costs, can be changed without much difficulty. Noncontrollable costs, or fixed costs, are difficult to change and are almost built in, e.g., rent and insurance. These costs are discussed in greater detail in Chapter 6.

DEPRECIATION

Depreciation expenses are arrived at through a process of allocating the costs of equipment, buildings, furniture, and fixtures to the years of their useful life. Depreciation does not require working capital or any payment, nor is it cash set aside. It is a tax shelter or deductible noncash expense for income tax purposes. The commercial foodservice may want to deduct the highest depreciation possible in any given year in order to lower taxable income.

There are basically four methods of depreciating assets, as defined below:

1. **Straight-Line Method**--This method distributes the costs of an asset equally over each year of its useful life. For example, assume that a convection oven costs $5500 and is expected to have eight years of service and then have a trade-in value at the end of eight years of $300. The trade-in value is subtracted from the cost and the answer is divided by eight years:

    $$\frac{\$5500 - \$300 = \$5200}{8 \text{ years}} = \$650 \text{ annual depreciation expense}$$

2. **Units-Produced Method** -- The depreciation is based on number of products produced. For example, if an oven is expected to have 100,000 baking hours in its life, the price of the oven less the trade-in value is

divided by 100,000. Each year is charged depreciation based on the estimated number of hours used that particular year.

$$\frac{\$5500 \ - \ \$300 \ = \ \$5200}{100,000} = \ 5.2¢ \text{ depreciation for every hours of operation}$$

3. **Declining-Balance Method** -- The depreciation rate is based on double the value when a straight-line method is used. If the life is expected to be eight years (on a straight line 12.5% each year), the declining balance is doubled at 25%. See Exhibit 2.8. This method ignores salvage value.

Exhibit 2.8   Example of a Declining Balance Depreciation

Year	Annual Depreciation	Net Book Value
1	$5500 x .25 = $1,375	$5500 - $ 1375 = $4,125
2	$4,125 x .25 = $1,031	$4,125 - $ 1031 = $3,095
3	$3,094 x .25 = $774	$3,095 - $774 = $2,321
4	$2,321 x .25 = $580	$2,321 - $580 = $1,741
5	$1,741 x .25 = $435	$1,741 - $435 = $1,306
6	$1,306 x .25 = $327	$1,306 - $327 = $ 979
7	$979 x .25 = $245	$979 - $245 = $ 734
8	$734 x .25 = $184	$734 - $184 = $ 550

4. **Sum-of-the-Years' Digits Method**--The years of the item's life are added together, e.g., if 10 years' life expectancy, the sum of the years is 55 (10 + 9 + 8 + 7 + 6 + 5 + 4 + 3 + 2 + 1). The first year 10/55 of the cost less salvage value could be depreciated ($5,500 x 10/55 = $1,000). The simplest and most frequently used method is the straight-line depreciation one.

FINANCIAL TRENDS

A manager who is well trained in financial management will pick up on trends and identify the red flags. Key revenue figures and expenditure figures should be tracked from month to month. The items suggested are:

- Cash on hand compared to payables. What is the difference between accounts payable and cash on hand?

- Assets compared to liabilities. What is the difference between assets and liabilities? The liquidity of a company is measured by the ratios of current liabilities to current assets, as follows:

$$\frac{\text{Current Assets}}{\text{Current Liabilities}} = \text{Current Ratio}$$

- Accounts receivable. Are receivables increasing or decreasing? How effective is the collection procedure? How many accounts receivables are over 30 days old? It is important to know the average time that accounts receivable are outstanding, or the average collection period. That is measured by figuring the accounts receivable ratio, for example:

$$\frac{\text{Net Accounts Receivable}}{\text{Net Service Revenue}} \div 365 = \text{Accounts Receivable Ratio}$$

- Value of inventory. How many days of inventory are on hand? "Just in time" is certainly the goal. Reduce inventory and reduce costs.

- Percent of food costs to sales. Does percentage fluctuate? Why?

- Labor costs compared to sales. Is the cost of labor increasing faster than sales?

Performance should be measured against the control elements (amounts established) in the budget. These comparisons, if done regularly and on a timely basis, will show trends and forecast trouble before it is too late to do something about it. An accounting system that provides managers timely financial reports that directors/managers can analyze for trends and warnings of potential problems makes it possible to control costs. There is increased meaning to performance measurement when comparisons are made-- present week with past week, present month with past month, and present year with past year.

SALES AND CASH CONTROL

Good financial management is possible if certain steps are taken and controls are in place. The reports mentioned earlier are the results of the action taken in handling sales and cash. The reports do not do the controlling. Management needs good procedures for accounting for sales, for handling cash, for paying bills, and for banking. Some of the elements or tools needed are:

Bank reconciliation
Cash-handling procedures
Point-of-sale system
Procedures for coding invoices

Each of these elements is described below.

Point-of-Sale System

Point-of-sale systems are discussed in Chapter 7, "Using Technology in Controlling Costs," as to the type of system and what is possible. Basic information is required from the point-of-sale system--whether the foodservice operation is computerized or uses an old 1940s cash register. The basic information needed includes the following:

- Total sales for the meal/period--for evaluating how much each meal or category contributed to the total revenue

- Sales tax information--for filing tax reports and determining amounts due

- Numbers of customers served--for forecasting and scheduling of staff

- Average check per meal--when not provided by the point of sale, arrived at by dividing the number of customers served during a period of time into the total sales in dollars taken in for that same period of time

- Number of servings of each menu item sold--for checking with food production records (information from both sources can be used as a check and balance); this can indicate when slow-moving items should be removed from the menu and replaced with more popular items

Cash-Handling Procedures

A good cash-handling procedure cannot be over-emphasized. The handling of cash procedures should be established and followed without deviation. Checks and balances help keep people honest, and without these, management is asking for problems. Some of the safeguards suggested are as follows:

- Have a limited number of bonded people as custodians of monies in a safe; each should verify the last custodian's balance in the safe with that person at the start of the shift, and verify the balance upon leaving for the day with the next custodian present (if feasible) or with someone from upper management, who will initial the amount left in the safe.

- Train supervisory staff to operate the cash register when need necessitates, as operator can become ill suddenly or another such emergency can occur.

- Keep all monies in a locked safe or at the register(s) at all times until time of banking.

- Determine the specific amount of money that will be a "cashier's bank" or start up money (based on sales volume and known needs).

- Have the cashier and one person from management staff (or an approved designated person) count the cash drawer and see that any discrepancies are immediately resolved. Overages and underages should be recorded by the cashier, and steps taken to reduce or eliminate overages and underages; do not allow cashier to "fix underages by adding money when there is a shortage, or pocket money when there is an overage."

- Have individual register readings taken by a <u>non-operator of the cash register</u> (management or approved person) after each meal period; the cashier should not be aware of the reading amount until **after the cashier has counted the cash drawer**.

- Train cashiers in the proper way to give change and process checks. Refer to Exhibit 2.9 to see what a check should contain to be properly completed and acceptable.

- See that all sales are rung up at the point of sale.

Exhibit 2.9   Correctly Completed Check

1.   Person's name, address, and telephone number

2.   Current date

3.   Same as foodservice bank account

4.   Same as amount of the customer's check (may want a policy of DO NOT CASH CHECKS); handwritten dollar amount the same as the numerical amount

5.   Bank and address printed on check (a "real" check and not a promotional voucher)

6.   Signature on the check the same as the name printed at the top of the check

Preparing Bank Deposit

The goal in preparing a bank deposit should be to prepare money for deposit in the bank accurately, efficiently, and in a matter that will preclude the bank's finding discrepancies (shortages or overages). Each bank has its own procedures for deposits that should be followed. Use only preprinted bank deposit slips to avoid possible errors. Exhibit 2.10 provides an example of a completed form that is used by many school districts when counting money and preparing a bank deposit.

Exhibit 2.10   Example of a Completed Cashier/Banking Record

INTEAM FOOD SYSTEM
CASHIER/BANKING RECORD

Date: 5/30   **Restaurant:** Oscar's Bagel Shop

Currency Breakdown			Rolled Coins			
8	$20s	= $ 160	2	Quarters	x $10	= $ 20.00
6	$10s	= 60	3	Dimes	x $5	= 15.00
7	$ 5s	= 35	2	Nickels	x $2	= 4.00
21	$ 1s	= 21	4	Pennies	x $ .50	= 2.00

Total Currency $ 276

List of Checks

			Loose Coins			
General Goods	$ 280			Halves	x $ .50	= $ 5.00
	$			Quarters	x $ .25	= 1.50
	$			Dimes	x $ .10	= 1.50
	$			Nickels	x $ .05	= .40
	$			Pennies	x $ .01	= 0
	$			**Total Coins**		$ 49.40
	$					
	$					
	$					
	$					

Total Checks $ 280

Signature *Emily Miller*
Verifying Accuracy

Bank Bag Number   10

TOTAL DEPOSIT $ 605.40

Signature *J. Jones*
Verifying Accuracy
Person Taking to Bank *JJ*

Source: Pannell-Martin, D., and G. Applebaum, *inTEAM Food System Manager's Manual.* Alexandria, VA: inTEAM Associates, Inc, 1995.

The following procedures will help accomplish the goal:

- Have two or more people count and roll or wrap money (if bank requires and as bank prescribes).

- Place all bills face upward; put same denominations together, e.g., all $10 bills together.

- Count all remaining change that is not wrapped, put in envelope, and record amount on outside of envelope according to denominations, e.g.:

3 x 50¢	=	$ 1.50
10 x 25¢	=	2.50
9 x 10¢	=	.90
4 x 5¢	=	.20
30 x 1¢	=	.30
Totals		$ 5.40

- Stamp wrapped money and envelope with name on bank account, and date.

- Complete a form similar to the one in Exhibit 2.10, which records the amount of money in each denomination; have two people verify the amounts and denominations of money and sign or initial that the amount in the bank deposit is correct as counted; insert a copy of the record of deposit with money in a bank bag; keep a copy for your records.

- Ask to see the bank teller's deposit tape when the bank finds a discrepancy; the bank teller's tape should match the dollar amounts as they appear on form in Exhibit 2.10; if the tape is different, the discrepancy can be traced.

Bank Reconciliation

The bank statement should be reconciled with the operation's records monthly. There should be an explanation for any differences between the bank's cash balance and the bookkeeper's records. Differences are usually due to one or more of the following reasons:

- Deposit in transit (a deposit made on the last day of the month but not recorded in the month)

- Checks written to pay expenditures that haven't cleared the bank

- Bounced check(s)

- Bank service charges

- Interest that the account earned

Procedures for Coding Invoices

In order to evaluate data and divide out costs by categories, the invoices need to be processed in a manner that identifies what they are for. Establish categories and a numerical code system that designates the different categories; e.g., alcoholic beverages, meats, bakery/baked goods, dairy products, staples, produce. If there are more than one kitchen, it will be important to designate which kitchen and keep the accounts separate.

Invoices or delivery tickets should be signed by an authorized person (s) verifying that the product listed is the product received. Credit slips should be completed in duplicate at the time of receipt when products are not received that are listed on the invoice. A suggested credit form (Exhibit 5.10) appears in Chapter 5, "Controlling Food Costs."

The invoices that have been coded can be entered into the accounting system for payment and as a part of the profit and loss statement in the proper category. These categories become very important when evaluating/analyzing costs. For example, if food costs are higher than the norm set at one unit, food can be broken down by categories and it can be determined where the costs are high.

Ratio analyses help in comparing and analyzing the food costs. For example, what percent of the revenue is being spent for meats? for produce?

This chapter has highlighted the main procedures needed to control costs from management's standpoint.

3
SETTING PRICES AND DETERMINING REVENUE AVAILABLE

CONTENTS

OBJECTIVES OF CHAPTER 3

After studying this chapter, the reader should be able to:

- Demonstrate methods of determining appropriate prices to charge
- Determine when and how to effectively increase prices
- Calculate revenue available
- Identify innovative ways of increasing revenue or sales
- Identify ways to help eliminate theft
- Determine actions necessary to ensure the accomplishment of a monetary net gain.

Setting the right prices and determining how much revenue is available are important, indeed essential, to financial planning and success. Setting prices--not too high and yet high enough--takes knowing a lot about the customer and potential customer as well as knowing a lot about the costs; however, determining revenue available sounds easy. For some foodservices that is not true; for example, a hospital, correctional facility, or nursing home may be receiving "X" dollars per day for meals--and the site foodservice manager may not be directly involved in how much will be available to operate on.

The schools that participate in the National School Lunch and Child Nutrition programs receive federal funds, and in many states there is a supplement from the state. Thus, to arrive at the revenue, the prices charged the customers and the federal and state funds received must be added together.

The B&I foodservices may be receiving a subsidy for employees that is a part of the revenue. Universities often have three to five payment plans, each for a different amount. Determining the revenue becomes complicated. College or university foodservices operate similarly to commercial free enterprise activities.

The foodservice director at a correctional facility or a health care operation may be totally functioning on a set budget. The director needs to determine how much is available and prorate it by meal or service. For example, if $8.56 per day is available, what portions can be allotted to breakfast, to lunch, to dinner, etc.?

SETTING PRICES

Most segments of the foodservice industry set prices and collect payment from the customers for the meals. Even those segments that operate on a given budget are setting the prices or deciding the revenue per meal without realizing it when requesting a certain amount in the budget.

The perception of good value for the money is one of the main goals and is a leading factor in a restaurant's or foodservice's success. If the customer thinks the prices are too high for what is received, the customer count decreases. Often the goal of management is to make as much profit as possible and to keep the customers coming back, whereby profit may be a high average check from a limited customer base or a small average check from a large customer base.

Consistency of food quality and portion size is an absolute must in setting prices, as well as in building a sound business.

Some good references that provide more detailed approaches to pricing and menu mixes for best returns are the following books: *Menu Pricing and Strategy* by Jack Miller, *Foodservice Organization by Marion Spears*, and *Menu Engineering* by M. L. Kasavana and Donald Smith. The menu controls everything, and planning a good menu is the secret to overall success, particularly financial success.

Where is that magical point in pricing? Depending on trial and error or a gut feeling about the "right price" to charge is dangerous. There are numerous approaches used when setting prices, and those most frequently used are discussed below.

Methods of Setting Prices

Method 1. Factor System

The factor system of pricing (cost-multiplier pricing strategy) is one of the most commonly used methods. The factor system is where a percentage of markups are used. It is based on the food cost and keeping food cost at a specific percentage of the sale price. The food is precosted using the recipe, and that cost is increased by a percentage to set the price. For example, if the desired food cost is 30%, divide 30 into 100 to determine the factor to use (multiply by) in setting the prices. The food costs are then multiplied by the factor to arrive at the price:

- 50% food cost, multiply by 2 = 50% markup
- 40% food cost, multiply by 2.5 = 60% markup
- 30% food cost, multiply by 3.33 = 70% markup
- 25% food cost, multiply by 4 = 75% markup

If the food cost is $2.50 and the desired food cost is 30%:

$2.50 food cost x 3.33 multiplier = $8.325 or $7.99 or $8.99[1]
selling price

The advantage to using this method is that it is so simple. There are, however, three big problems with the factor system: (1) labor is not

---

[1]May want to set selling price at $7.99 (below $8.325) or $8.99 (higher than $8.325) to avoid several different prices.

considered, (2) precosts and actual costs may not be the same (or close due to preparation methods, etc.), and (3) the perceived value may not be equal to what the customer expects--which is not based on a "uniform markup." For example, a serving of french fries will not cost more than 20¢, a food cost of 50% is desired (100 ÷ 50 = 2; multiply 20¢ x 2 = 40¢) a sale price of 40¢ is too low. That item could be priced at $1 and the customer would be happy because of the perceived value. Another example is a "homemade" cinnamon roll with food cost of 7¢--using the factor system would not include labor costs, which may be double the raw food cost.

Method 2. Actual Cost Plus Profit Margin

Actually pricing out the cost of food, labor, and miscellaneous and adding a set profit margin is used by some. With labor inching up beyond food costs, this is the method that helps ensure that all costs are covered. Management must decide what percent of the revenue will be spent for food and labor. The formula then becomes:

Actual food cost + actual labor cost x factor = selling price

$2.50 food cost + $1.95 labor cost = $4.45
30% + 20% = 50% (100% ÷ 50% = 2 multiplier)
$4.45 x 2 = $8.90 or $8.99 selling price

Precosting should be updated on a regular basis, e.g., once every three months. This means clocking the preparation time and multiplying that by the average cost of the labor hour (see Chapter 5 for how to determine the average cost of a labor hour). The productivity may have changed, and the actual cost of preparing the products may be greater than previously thought. Once all the costs have been determined, this actual cost plus a profit margin should be compared to the price charged.

The problem with this method of pricing is that perceived value is not considered. The actual cost may be greater than the customer will pay and yet the item may be a good customer attraction and may need to be considered a "loss leader" and priced low.

Method 3. Highest Price or Gross Profit

Using the highest price or gross profit method is an interesting way of operating. Often a prime spot/location may cause management to use this method of pricing--the highest price that can be charged is set. What is left determines what can be spent for food and labor and what will be the profit.

This method of pricing is used primarily in the restaurant industry especially among upscale restaurants. Or, it may be used when the management of a restaurant knows the customers have the money and are willing to pay to eat there. Also, it may be used when a foodservice wants to group prices and wants to be known for all meals being priced at a set amount, e.g., a restaurant where all meals are priced at $21.95.

Method 4. Reasonable Price or Base Price

Setting the reasonable price, base price, or fair pricing, or setting the desirable price is like the opposite of "highest price or gross profit." This method is used in the extreme by school boards when setting meal prices for schools. The prices often are set without any consideration for the actual cost of producing the meal. Then management must find a way of keeping costs within that price. This method forces the amount that can be spent on food rather than the price charged being based on costs.

Method 5. Texas Restaurant Association

The Texas Restaurant Association's method of setting prices considers fully all costs and the desired profit margin. Raw food cost (arrived at by precosting) is treated as the fixed cost, and all other costs and profit margins are variable costs and expressed in percentage.

100% = Menu Selling Price
100% - %Labor Cost (LC) + %Other Cost (OC) + %Profit Margin (PM) =
Menu Selling Price (MSP)
100% - LC + OC + PM = %MSP Used Up

For example, 25% LC + 15% OC + 12% PM = 52 % of MSP .
If raw food cost (FC) is $4, the MSP would have to be $8.34 or $8.49 as shown below.

$$\frac{\$4 \text{ FC}}{100\% \text{ MSP} - 52\% = 48\% \text{ or } .48} = \$8.34 \text{ MSP or } \$8.49[1]$$

---

[1] Management often groups items to avoid several different prices, e.g., two or three different menu items at $8.49 or $8.99 and another group of menu items at $9.49 or $9.99.

Method 6. Non-Structured or Intuitive Price or Forced Food Cost

Some managers take risks and set prices based on intuition. With precosting and checking competitors' prices, this method could be dangerous--a trial and error approach. The price that will be charged is set, and then how much is available for food and labor costs is determined on a percentage basis. The price may be set based on competition's prices or management's thinking of what is reasonable or what will go in the area.

Method 7. Combination

The combination method considers the actual cost, perceived value, and desired profit margin. This is the hardest method and requires knowing the customer and the business.

The right price is the one the customer will pay. There is a lot of psychology behind reaching that right price. A combination of all the mentioned methods seems to be the best approach. Exhibit 3.1 illustrates how the combination method can be used when pricing.

In Exhibit 3.1, labor costs have not been identified, but the amount of labor each food item would require is noted with "X," representing very little time required, to "XXX," which denotes a lot of time required to prepare and/or clean up.

One factor not shown above is "what the traffic will bear" or what the customer considers "fair value." Also, some items may be made available as a service and not have much of a profit margin. For example, yogurt in Exhibit 3.1 has high food cost and yet the price charged is above the competition (grocery stores' prices).

The cost of food, as well as labor and overhead, should be considered when establishing the actual cost. The surest way of costing out labor is with measuring productivity--exactly how much time it takes to prepare the product using a stop watch. The time it takes is divided by the number of servings to determine minutes. Not many foodservices do these detailed calculations. Chapter 4 provides examples of measuring productivity.

The cost of labor is hard to calculate; thus the following chart will give consideration to all aspects when pricing.

Exhibit 3.1 Example of Using the Combination Method of Pricing for a Cafeteria or Convenience Store

Food Items (1)	Food Cost (2)	Labor Cost (3)	Current Price Charged (4)	Prices Charged by Competition (5)	Pro- posed Price (6)	% of Food Cost (7)
Coffee, Cup	$ .12	XX	$ .75	FF $ .79	$1	12%
Fresh Fruit, Medium	$ .20	X	$ .49	CS $ .69	$ .69	29%
Milk Shake, 12 oz.	$ .17	XXX	$ .79	FF $ 1.09	$ .99	17%
Sandwiches, Cold Cuts	$ .43	XX	$ .99	CS $ 1.39	$ 1.29	33%
Pretzel, Soft 2 oz.	$ .22	XX	$ .79	SM $ 1.00	$ .99	23%
Yogurt, 8 oz.	$ .39	X	$ .79	GS $ .59	$ .89	44%
Popcorn, Medium	$ .18	XX	$ .75	SM $ 1.25	$ 1	18%

Abbreviations used to designate source of prices in column 5:

CS = convenience stores
FF = fast- food restaurants
GS = grocery stores
SM = shopping malls

Pricing as a Marketing Technique

Pricing may be used as a marketing technique: (1) to bring customers in with hopes of selling more, (2) to increase revenue on particular days of the week or times of the year, e.g., two for the price of one on Tuesday night, and (3) to increase revenue at particular hours of the day, e.g., early bird special.

How items are priced may be a determining factor with the customer and can increase sales. Some of the other factors are listed below:

"Loss leader."--Occasionally there is a need for using "loss leader" pricing as a marketing device. "Loss leaders" are items priced below normal markup to pull in the customers, e.g., "early bird" dinner menus and prices; in early 1997 McDonald's promoted the Big Mac at 55¢ with the purchase of a coke and french fries.

Table d' hote.--When table d' hote pricing is used, a complete meal price is establish. With this arrangement it is important to cost out all the entrees and side dish options and establish one price that will cover all the choices.

Group pricing.--Group pricing sets a category of food at the same price. For example, it is common to have group pricing of entrees. In a cafeteria, there may be a group of entrees priced at $1.99 and a group priced at $2.99. And, all vegetables may be at the same price even though the costs differs.

A la carte pricing.--A la carte pricing is needed for most food offerings. Regardless of the options, there will be the customers who want something different. A la carte pricing is usually a little higher than the complete meal pricing. When the prices have been set, each menu that combines foods needs to be priced out using the a la carte pricing--as a check of the prices. The menu price should offer a slight savings over prices for each item individually.

INCREASING PRICES

Increasing prices is often the remedy management jumps on when the profit margin is not at the desired levels. This can be very shortsighted. It may mean pricing oneself out of business. There are a number of factors to be considered before increasing prices, such as:

- Economic situation in the area at the time
  (Can the customer afford to pay more? Will the customer pay more?)
- What competition charges
  (Are your prices really too low? Will you price yourself out of the business?)
- When prices were last increased
- Whether reducing costs has been considered

- What the customer considers fair value
- Whether price adjustments will permit the reduction of some prices, while others are increased
- How increases can be made less noticeable

Since customers expect more when prices go up, foodservice management should try to disguise increased prices or avoid attention being brought to increased prices. D. Pavesic (1988) in *Indirect Cost Factors in Menu Pricing* provides suggestions to restaurant management regarding pricing menu items; some highlights of the suggestions are as follows:

- Consider increasing portions or accompaniments to create a "new" and "improved" item and give it a new name.

- Re-position items that have been noticeably increased to less visible parts of the menu and emphasize lower-price substitutes in their place.

  (With a tri-fold menu the customer focuses on the center panel menu first, next on the right-hand corner and then on the left-hand corner.)

- Never raise prices across the board. It is better to raise only a few items with each reprinting of the menu.

- Do not align prices in a continuous pattern, and never list menu items in price sequence.

Psychology needs to be used when changing prices. When psychologically will be the best time to raise prices? Certainly not during Christmas holidays or at tax time. With universities/colleges and schools the prices are best raised over the summer. If the menu, presentation/packaging, and atmosphere are changed, the price increases may go unnoticed. Price increases are less noticed if the product is served or "packaged" differently, e.g., Bay Street Restaurant lowered food costs by reducing the number of shrimp on a meal and changed it from shrimp on rice to shrimp on pasta.

Restaurants' price increases often go unnoticed. Olive Garden took an item off the menu and re-introduced a slightly different product under a new name at a higher price. Ideally, a price increase would go unnoticed. The B-Line Restaurant in the Peabody Hotel in Orlando (FL) totally changes the looks of its menus annually, maintaining a few favorites and introducing new ones. This provides an opportunity to revitalize the food served and increase prices as needed.

Should the news media pick up on price increases, management needs to be able to justify them. It is wise to prepare a media release and have it ready in case it is needed.

Will a price increase cause a loss of customers? If so, what will the price increase yield? Is it better to keep the customer count high or to reduce numbers of customers and increase the profit margin on each customer check? These are difficult questions to answer.

DETERMINING REVENUE AVAILABLE

How much revenue is available for breakfast, lunch, and dinner? Some managers are not involved in setting prices, but are given a budget or the prices are set for them. Schools, subsidized B&Is, health cares, prisons, and universities/colleges have more complex budgets made up of board sales, cash sales, snack bars, banquets, etc., and some more than one source of revenue.

The revenue available varies greatly, as can be seen by the chart in Exhibit 3.2. Within each of these categories there is a variance. For example, schools may charge an average of $1 for breakfast and $1.75 for lunch. However, the breakfast foods at a hospital foodservice for non-patients are traditionally priced a la carte.

Exhibit 3.2 Examples of the Average Check

Meals/Services	Noncommercial	Commercial Medium-Price Range
Breakfast	$ 3.70	$ 7.50
Lunch	$ 5.60	$ 12.75
Dinner	$ 6.50	$ 15.75

Schools

All school breakfasts and lunches served to students in compliance with federal and state regulations under the National School Lunch and Child Nutrition Programs qualify for federal subsidies or reimbursements and USDA donated commodities. Exhibit 3.3 provides an example of the breakfast revenue in the 1998-99 for a typical school district. Exhibit 3.4 provides an example of the lunch revenue in 1998-99 school year.

The federal reimbursement rates increase annually and are announced in July of each year in the Federal Register. Some states subsidize the breakfast program, some the lunch program, and some neither. Local school districts occasionally establish a per-meal subsidy , but this is the exception. Many districts subsidize the foodservice program unwillingly because the programs are running deficits. As educational budgets have tightened, school boards have started expecting more to be paid by the foodservice programs.

Exhibit 3.3   Example of the Revenue for a School Breakfast Under the Child Nutrition Program

| SOURCE (1) | ELEMEN-TARY PAYING STUDENT (2) | SECOND-ARY PAYING STUDENT (3) | FREE | | REDUCED-PRICE | | ADULT (8) |
			Regular (4)	Severe Need (5)	Regular (6)	Severe Need (7)	
Cash Sales	$ .75	$ .85	N/A	N/A	$ .3000	$.3000	$1.30
Federal Reimburse-ment[1]	.20	.20	$ 1.0725	$1.2775	.7725	.9775	-0-
Local Funds	- 0 -	- 0 -	- 0 -	- 0 -	- 0 -	- 0 -	- 0 -
State Matching Funds[2]	.02	.02	.0200	.0200	.0200	.0200	- 0 -
TOTALS	$ .97	$1.07	$1..0925	$1.2975	$1.0925	$1.2975	$1.30

[1]Federal reimbursement rates increase annually and are announced in July of each year.

[2]Check your state for possible revenue.

Exhibit 3.4   Example of the Revenue for a Lunch Under the National School Lunch Program

SOURCE (1)	ELEMEN- TARY PAID LUNCH (2)	SECOND- ARY PAID LUNCH (3)	FREE LUNCH (4)	REDUCED- PRICE LUNCH (5)	ADULT LUNCH (6)
Cash Sales	$1.5000	$1.7500	- 0 -	$ .4000	$2.25
Federal Reimbursement[1]	.1800	.1800	$1.9425	1.5425	-0-
Entitlement Commodity Value[1]	.1475	.1475	.1475	.1475	- 0 -
State Matching Funds[2]	.0600	.0600	.0600	.0600	- 0 -
Local Funds	- 0 -	- 0 -	- 0 -	- 0 -	- 0 -
TOTALS	$1.8875	$2.1375	$2.1500	$2.1500	$2.25

Universities/Colleges

In the universities and colleges the revenue available for each meal is complicated by the different board plans and pricing methods. Management needs a lot of data from prior years to aid in the setting of prices and then determining how much revenue on the average is available.

---

[1]Reimbursement rates and the commodity rate for 1997-98 were used. If a severe-need district, the rate of reimbursement would be greater. The reimbursement rates increase annually.

[2]Check your state for possible revenue. Only three states do not provide some matching funds. Some state matching funds may not show up as cash amounts for meals served.

Traditional board meal counts are declining in the college segment as they turn to nontraditional options like declining balances and debit cards.

An example of the different payment plans is illustrated at the University of North Carolina, which offers five plans of payment in 1998, as follows:

- **A La Carte Club Plan**--Students buy food on a per-item basis and also decide on the size of their debit accounts. Unused portions of plan are refunded at the end of the school year.

- **Value or Carte Blanche Plan**--Unlimited all-you-can-eat dining is provided and is popular with boys and students who stay on campus and want full meals. The cost was set at $1,350 for the 1998-99 school year.

- **Value or Traditional Club Plan**--This flex-type program is offered as 12 a week (for first year student with $425 flex), 12 a week (other students; $325 flex dollar option) and 5 a week, priced from $535 to $1485 per semester in 1998-99 with varying a la carte options.

- **Block Club Plan**--Students in the 150, 100, and 75 blocks choose 150, 100, and 75 meals and $325 flex dollar option. It is priced at $1160 (150 meals), $925 (100 meals), or $785 (75 meals) a semester in the 1998-99 school year. There are no restrictions on when and where this plan is used.

- **Cash Payment**--Student pays for what is received at the time of service.

The University of Georgia has only three plans, and they are:

1. 7-Day Plan--unlimited food and snacks Monday through Sunday (no Sunday evening meal) for $1,884 (in 1997-98 for 9 months), averaging $8.29 per day, based on students eating meals on campus 227.3 days, or 84% of the time.

2. 5-Day Plan--unlimited food and snacks Monday through Friday for $1,704 (in 1997-98 for 9 months), averaging $10.27 per day based on students eating on campus 165.9 days, or 92.2% of the time.

3. Cash Plan--unlimited food and snacks (in 1997-98--$3.85 for breakfast, $5.05 for lunch, and $6.60 for dinner).

Like some other foodservice operations, those in schools, colleges and universities need to determine what the average revenues are for each meal because of "no shows." Do most university students go home on weekends or is it popular to stay on campus for the weekend events? This may vary from season to season.

Business and Industry

Business and industry (B&I) foodservices often run several different revenue-generating operations. In most instances, some of revenue generated by other services are used to subsidize the cafeteria services. Only about 40% of the B&Is operate subsidized foodservices today. Those that do subsidize provide anywhere from a few dollars up to 60% of the costs. For many years upper management has directed that the prices charged by most of the B&I units be barely above costs because of the desire to keep the company employees "in house" at meal time. Also, the employees expect the prices to be less than they would pay on the outside. However, in today's changing world, the majority of the B&I operations either operate on a break-even basis or are required to return a small profit to the business.

The B&I foodservice manager needs to determine where the revenue is coming from--shift workers, white collar workers and blue collar workers. If branded products or stations (station serving well-known products) are in place it is wise to prepare a profit and loss statement on each of the different stations. E.g., determine the percentage of the total revenue from each service:

Cafeteria service	66%
Executive dining	5%
Catering	18%
Vending	8%
Other services	3%
	100%

Health Cares

The revenue available in health care units varies greatly, depending on who operates the foodservices and the source of the revenue. For example, what proportion of the revenue is patient meals? How much is from non-patients? E.g.,

$27,000 patient meals	60%
18,000 non-patient meals	40%
$45,000 total meals	100%

It is probably advisable to totally separate patient meals and non-patient meals (public dining). The reasons are that patient meals are based on operating costs, whereas the public dining portion should be treated as a commercial restaurant because it receives no subsidy and could not continue functioning with a loss.

Reimbursement systems most often used are (1) fee-for-service and (2) capitated payments. In the case of the fee-for-service system, the payer determines the price for the service and which services are to be provided.

Restaurants

In restaurants it is simple to determine the revenue when all meals are priced for cash payment. However, accepting a variety of credit cards usually increases revenue. The fees charged and the availability of the money have to be considered. Credit cards are being accepted by many segments of the foodservice industry but may add some reduction in revenue and some complications. VISA, Master Card, and Discover credit cards are the most popular. This is because they are bank card accounts and are accepted by the banks as a part of the deposit, a charge is made by the bank for the processing--1.5-3.5 percent generally. Diners Club and American Express are not bank cards. Drafts have to be sent to the companies for reimbursement, and a fee of 3-5 percent is charged.

Correctional Institutions

In correctional institutions the amount of revenue is generally established by the institution's budget. Unfortunately, the revenue doesn't always increase as the number of inmates increases. The manager needs to break down the revenue by person and by meal.

INCREASING REVENUES/SALES

All segments of the foodservice industry use increases in sales as one criterion for judging success. The competition has become so keen in recent years in some parts of the country that the market is over-saturated with restaurants, and increasing revenue or sales require more and more creative approaches. Some creative approaches are described below.

Universities/Colleges

Many universities and colleges do not offer board-plan meals, e.g., University of Maryland, University of Miami, Boston College, Dartmouth College, and University of Nebraska. Their food is cash at the points of sale.

University of Miami, for example, closed its board plan cafeterias and replaced them with fresh, scatter-system design stations and with a multi-brand food court. They expanded and relocated the C-Store, converted snack bars to carry-out units, and created a wellness center complete with juice bar to capitalize on the "healthy" trend. They consolidated and downsized administration from several offices to one. The increased sales and decreased cost of upper management and manning of offices has enabled them to contribute $400,000 more to general funds.

Health Care Facilities

Special room services work for some in affluent health care facilities. Gourmet dinners are served, to patients as well as guests. Dinners may offer the option of wine. The volume and price must be high enough to make these facilities profitable.

Wine and cheese carts in the late afternoon have proven very popular in some nursing homes; some others offer "Shirley Temple" type drinks with hors d'oeuvres.

In some hospitals ,express or self-service bars not only have increased sales but have decreased labor costs. For example, St. Agnes Hospital in White Plains, NY, a 184-bed facility, offers pizza as a regular on the "Express Bar." The self-service bars have caused sales to go up, and top-your-own pizza and "grab-and-go" meals have removed "labor intense" as a description of the offering.

Correctional Institutions

Some correctional facilities are charging inmates for food or requiring them to work for their food. For example, in St. Lucie County, FL, the correctional facility charges the inmates $1.20 a day for food. This is not the norm.

In 1996 the federal government started a new policy for inmates of federal prisons that charges the equivalent of $21,000 a year. There is no report yet from the Bureau of Prisons on how well this works.

The Bernalillo County Detention Center in Albuquerque, NM, is piloting a charge of $40 a day to inmates for room and board. The inmates can work off the charge. The $11,000 this program will generate will help with the costs of incarceration. This is an innovative approach to funding a budget.

Ideas that Apply to All

Listed below are some approaches for increasing revenue that nearly every segment of the industry could use.

● Meals on Wheels and Congregate Meals

Meals for senior citizens and those who are alone and/or sick have much potential as the need increases and expands across the country. In 1996-97 the meals were bringing in between $2.75 and $3.75 to foodservice operations.

- Home Meal Replacement (HMR) Foodservice

Home Meal Replacement (HMR), one of the most talked-about foodservice opportunities of the late 90s, is expected to see strong growth over the next five years. It is popular with those who are time-short-convenience-oriented. HMRs have possibilities for all--even foodservices operating in child care centers, hospitals, and universities/schools; e.g. among the HMR items Wood Company sells to customers are pizzas (baked and unbaked), pastry/bakery items, pre-prepared fresh fruits and vegetables, rotisserie chicken, and side orders.

Eatzi is a new HMR operation developed by Phil Romano in partnership with the Brinker International organization (Dallas). It provides a lesson in how to capture this business using the food preparation environment with the chefs preparing fresh foods as part of the displays, as well as the "wares." A short-term bakery promotion is announced frequently, and the promotion changes as items come out of the ovens before your eyes. Mr. Romano's secret is that he has matched the selections, packaging, and service to the demographics of the market. Eatzi is located amid some of the most affluent and "time-short" consumers in a major city. He depends heavily on cross-merchandising to boost sales; e.g., products like milk (half-gallon) are priced competitively with the grocery store whereas the money is made on the gourmet-stuffed pork chops.

To-Go Dinner Party , a form of HMR, has developed into something more than ordering a pizza to go. A dinner party's food is being picked up fully or partially cooked, or even raw, with directions on how to finish at home. Hosts or hostesses who work all day and want to impress guests with dinner at home often get the help they need from the foodservices in the building where they work.

- New Business

Some foodservices located in businesses and industries have opened as restaurants to the public. This has potential for foodservices located in hospitals and on college and school campuses.

- Vending

  Vending services are less labor-intensive than any of the other methods of service--and they take less space. Some machines are using debit cards quite effectively.

  There are basically four ways of operating vending services:

  - Contract with company for machines and services
  - Lease machines then fill and manage them
  - Own and manage machines
  - Obtain use of soda machines with purchase of products

  Owning and managing machines generally will yield the best return. Some drink machines are probably as profitable when the machines are provided with the purchase of drinks as when owned by the foodservices.

Other Creative Ways of Increasing Sales

There is no end to the creative ways the foodservice industry has found, and will continue to find, to increase sales/revenue. Some ways of increasing revenue are the obvious and the not so obvious, as follows:

1. Selective price increases or an across-the-board increase

2. Company store; gift shop

3. On-site periodic vendor sales -- jewelry, leather, plants, items to meet special occasions, e.g., valentine candy

4. Suggestive selling (encouraging the customer to purchase something)

5. Two for one and one penny pricing (obtain a second "one" for 1 cent more)

6. Bakeed items--cookies or specialty pies as "take home sale"

7. Catering company barbecues

8. New products introduced and marketed

9.   Cashless system; use of debit cards

10. Conceptual changes; de-institutionalizing the facility

11. Menu revisions -- new items, packaging, prices

12. Using branded foods (nationally known products)--often helping to bring prices charged up to those charged on the outside

13. Patio dining; outside barbecues

14. Food on carts or in kiosks in remote areas

15. Mobile coffee/pastry service in the morning, mobile wine/snacks in the afternoon

16. Theme meals

17. "Wholesale" food sales to employees

18. Upscale desserts and upscale prices

19. Gourmet entrees featured

20. Afternoon ice cream socials

21. Food sold by ounce/pound--salad, deli bar, frozen yogurt

22. Expanded hours of operation

23. Discontinuing unprofitable services and replacing with new offers, e.g., discontinuing executive dining room in health care or B&I facilities and replacing with express carts

24. Sales to outside customers and other foodservice facilities, e.g., schools, health cares, small restaurants, Meals on Wheels program, and congregate meal sites (in 1996 the programs were paying $2.75 to $3.75 per meal)

25. Providing services, e.g., photo processing, shoe repair, dry cleaning

26. Leasing space in foodservices to brand-name foods (e.g., Pizza Hut kiosk)

27. Advertising

CONTROLLING REVENUE/PREVENTING THEFT

Eliminating or preventing theft is a part of management's responsibility that may be unpleasant (and challenging). Several steps to eliminating or preventing theft will be discussed here.

Checks and balances should be in place to avoid opportunities for theft. Some basic controls should be incorporated into the handling of cash, as listed below:

● Guest checks should match with cash drawer or cash register.

● An overall supervisor should verify or correct what operators report. If someone other than the owner counts the cash money, there should be two people involved in the counting. They should both sign the record of the breakdown of the bank bag and insert one copy of the record with the money. Having one person controlling too much should be avoided. For example, avoid the same person requesting food from the kitchen, delivering food to tables, totaling the checks, and collecting payments. It is best to divide responsibilities among two or more people.

● Receipts should be deposited in a bank daily.

● Cashiers should be trained to handle money correctly.

● If checks are to be accepted, cashiers should be trained in steps for approving checks.

Employee Theft

According to a former president of the Chicago Professional Polygraph Department, approximately 17 percent of all employees can be classified as significantly dishonest. Some of the theft-prone areas and precautions are listed below.

- Waitperson omits from check some of the foods served to encourage a better tip. Some of the computerized systems match products sold to income received when the waitperson places the order with the kitchen.

- Waitperson uses same guest check for more than one customer and keeps money difference. Number all guest checks and put time of day on guest checks; keep guest checks safely stored.

- Waitperson or cashier destroys guest check and keeps money. Make certain guest checks and cash drawer balance, and check numbers on checks. Give each waitperson his or her numbered series of checks and see that all numbers in series are in sequence.

- Waitperson improperly totals check to inflate it. Electronically created checks have helped to eliminate a lot of such problems in the past.

These are some basic precautions that are needed, such as bond all employees who handle money. A computerized income control system can help make it nearly impossible for a waitperson or cashier to rip off the operation. The system should:

Verify Product Sold	with	Guest Check Totals	with	Sales Receipts	with	Sales Deposits

Such a system would require an order through the system to authorize the kitchen to prepare the food. No product would be issued from the kitchen or bar unless there is a written record issued.

- There is employee theft of foods, beverages, and supplies from inventory. Storage areas should be secured with tight controls in place since these are areas prone to theft. There are some basic rules that management should put into place, such as:

1. Physically inventory key items daily (or at the end of each shift) and compare the quantity used with the production record and the customer checks

2. Do not allow employees to take leftovers home

3. Keep storeroom locked except when products are being removed

4. Maintain a low inventory

5. Discourage employees from bringing in or carrying out large bags

6. Keep a good production record of each day's operation

Customer Theft

Customer theft exists in many forms, such as:

- "Walk the bill" or "walkouts" (the customer leaves without paying)

- Gives bad checks

- Uses invalid credit cards

- Are quick change artists

- Carry off all kinds of items from the table

- Doesn't want to pay for the meal because it "wasn't good" (after having nearly finished the meal)

Preventing customer theft from occurring is nearly impossible and requires more than just a manager's watchful eye. The employees have to be involved by giving close attention to the customers, which discourages theft.

Distributor Theft

Good receiving practices will help prevent distributor theft. Only trained and management-authorized people should receive deliveries. Each delivery needs to be checked against the order, counted and/or weighed, checked for quality, and signed for. The prices charged should be checked against the prices quoted, and the extensions (e.g., multiplication of quantities by unit prices, totaling the bills/invoices) should be checked.

4
CONTROLLING LABOR COSTS

CONTENTS

OBJECTIVES OF CHAPTER 4

After studying this chapter, the reader should be able to:

- Identify what makes up labor costs
- Measure productivity
- Apply basic formulas to staff a foodservice operation
- Determine the percentage of revenues/sales used for labor
- Identify ways of increasing productivity
- Determine the real cost of a labor hour
- Determine ways of reducing labor costs

Controlling labor costs is one of foodservice management's biggest challenges. The foodservice industry is very labor-intensive with low productivity--approximately 50 percent of the employee's time is used productively. For example, if the average cost of a labor hour is $8.50 (including fringe benefits and employer taxes), the average (real) cost of a productive hour of work may be costing $17 or more.

According to the National Restaurant Association's 1997 *Restaurant Industry Operations Report,* salaries and employee benefits are running an average of 31.1% to 31.9% of sales in full service restaurants, which is an improvement over the prior year's report. Fast-food restaurants are running 27.9%. The other segments of the industry report equally as much or more on labor costs. (These percentages were arrived at by dividing the labor costs by the total revenue/sales.)

Self-operated institutional foodservices and small operations often have high labor costs because of paying higher salaries and fringe benefits than commercially operated and chain operations. That is because they are often overstaffed and/or pay higher salaries and benefits to long term employees. Higher labor costs of self-operated units have enabled the commercial management companies to take over many of the self-operated foodservices in universities/colleges, businesses and industries (B&Is), schools, and hospitals.

Not only do the bigger commercial chains and management companies tend to pay foodservice personnel less, they usually obtain higher productivity than self-operated foodservices. In most cases they have a standardized approach to managing--particularly staffing and scheduling of labor. They offer training programs and use established company guidelines for measuring productivity.

According to labor studies done by the researchers in the foodservice industry, e.g., the National Restaurant Association and other professional organizations, hourly foodservice salaries were up in 1995 by 48¢, or 5 percent; this trend of increasing hourly wages continued in 1996 and increased more overall in 1997 as minimum wage increases became totally effective. The national minimum wage rates of pay went from $4.25 to $4.75 as of October 1, 1996, then jumped another 40¢, to $5.15, as of September 1, 1997--slightly over a 21 percent increase within one year. This increase has resulted in elimination of 146,000 jobs and increased prices charged by 42% of the restaurants (within six months after increase in wages) according to a study commissioned by the National Restaurant Association.

Recent increases in the minimum wage, the low unemployment rate, and an increased need for service employees have forced many owners and managers to pay above minimum wage to attract new recruits/employees. Service employees are shopping around for the highest hourly rate of pay; for example, the lead cook at a respected high-volume restaurant joins a new company that raises his salary by 23 percent, from $6.60 per hour to $8 per hour.

Some states and cities are pushing legislation through their legislative systems that would require even higher wages. The AFL-CIO is backing several states' legislative efforts that would increase those states' minimum wages. Also, the unions are supporting mandated employer-paid health care for employees as well as other fringe benefits. States such as Missouri, Montana, and Oregon and cities like Denver and Houston are considering higher minimum wages. For example, Denver is considering $6.85 in 1998, and $7.15 in 1999. California's minimum wage of $5.75 may increase further (proposed $1 raise by January 1999).

As a result of the federally mandated minimum wage increases, many foodservice directors/managers have reduced the need for both skilled and unskilled labor. The low wages of the past allowed many foodservice operators to continue offering time-consuming foods on their menus. As a result of increased labor costs, more attention is being given to staffing and productivity. This chapter identifies what makes up labor costs and suggests some ways these costs can be reduced. Also discussed are several methods of measuring productivity and some staffing standards.

IDENTIFYING LABOR COSTS

Payroll costs refer to gross pay (before taxes), and labor costs refer to total costs related to employees. Generally, labor costs can be divided into two categories:

1. Permanent employees (core staff or skeleton crew) essential to operating--fixed costs

2. Part-time and substitute employees on a more flexible schedule (when needed)--variable costs

Restaurants often pay salaries only to management and some even pay the skeleton crew on an hourly basis. As turnover rates increase and labor shortages persist, more and more foodservices are putting a skeleton crew on payroll as a fixed cost to obtain loyalty and continuity.

The costs of the part-time employee may be much easier to figure; e.g., if an employee is paid $7 per hour and works a 20-hour week, the cost is $140 x approximately 10% taxes (Social Security, Medicare, and unemployment-- approximately $14.00) + cost of meal (e.g., $2.50 x number of meals 5 = $12.50) equals $166.50 a week.

The costs of permanent (full-time) employees are much more complex because of fringe benefits such as sick leave and vacation days. Labor costs include (1) salaries and wages, (2) fringe benefits, and (3) payroll taxes. More detailed labor costs include not only an employee's pay, but also many labor-related expenses, such as:

Social Security taxes (employer's share--6.2% in 1998)
Medicare taxes (employer's share--1.45% in 1998)
Group life insurance
Health insurance
Worker's compensation
Unemployment taxes
Vacation days
Sick leave
Employee meals
Employee training expenses
Breaks
Uniforms and laundry

The commercial segments of the foodservice industry generally keep labor costs to well below 40 percent of the revenue. Exhibit 4.1. shows the average cost of a labor hour across the restaurant industry.

Most self-operated, noncommercial foodservice operations' employees are paid on a pay scale 15 to 25 percent higher than the commercial market for foodservice workers. This is one of the main reasons for an increased use of commercial foodservice management companies in schools and B&Is. Regardless of the type of foodservice, the labor costs, including fringe benefits, should be kept under 50 percent of the revenue.

Exhibit 4.1 Survey of Wage Rates for Hourly Employees in the Restaurant Industry, 1997[1]

TYPE OF HOURLY EMPLOYEE (1)	MEDIUM HOURLY WAGE (2)	LOWEST HOURLY WAGE (MEDIAN) (3)	HIGHEST HOURLY WAGE (MEDIAN) (4)	LOWEST AVERAGE WAGE LOCALLY (5)[1]	HIGHEST HOURLY WAGE LOCALLY (6)[1]
Cook	$7.75	$ 7.00	$9.25		
Assistant Cook	$7.43	$6.50	$8.00		
Short-Order Cook	$6.65	$6.00	$7.50		
Baker	$7.75	$7.00	$8.50		
Food/Salad Preparation Person	$6.16	$6.00	$7.00		
Crew Person (Fast Food)	$5.50	$5.00	$6.15		
Crew Supervisor (Fast Food)	$6.67	$6.25	$7.50		
Cafeteria Server	$5.58	$5.51	$7.25		
Cashier	$6.00	$5.50	$6.50		
Dishwasher	$5.75	$5.25	$6.00		
Driver (Delivery)	$5.00	$5.00	$6.00		
Waiter/Waitress	$ 2.87	$2.65	$3.75		
Host/Hostess	$6.00	$5.50	$6.95		
Bartender	$5.75	$5.25	$6.50		

These wages are weighted based on average hourly wage reported by each respondent.
Note: This hourly wage information was collected in August 1997 after the federal minimum wage was increased on October 1, 1996, from $4.25 per hour to $4.75 per hour. It will be meaningful to complete columns 5 and 6 with current, local data or check with state restaurant association for the current state data. From: "Survey of Wage Rates for Hourly Employees, 1997. Reprinted with the permission of the National Restaurant Association.

---

[1]By adding local wages, a comparison with the industry wages can be made.

Administrative or Supervisory Staff

The trend today is to reduce administrative and supervisory staffs by broadening the span of control and making each individual more responsible for the results. What is a reasonable span of control for a specific foodservice? The formulas that formerly existed have been ignored as the trend of eliminating middle management has become a practice. Many corporate or administrative offices became overstaffed in the prosperous 1970s and 1980s. Exhibit 4.2 provides a typical large hospital foodservice operation organizational chart in the 1980s. Exhibit 4.3 shows how that organization chart has shrunk in the 1990s because of tighter budgets.

Administrative functions still require a large share of the labor costs. According to a survey made in 1996 by the National Restaurant Association, 18% to 21% of labor costs goes to general and administrative functions.

Production and Service Staff

Careful scheduling of production and service staffs is one of the secrets to controlling labor costs. The number of labor hours is generally divided into three basic categories of duties:

- Food production
- Service
- Sanitation/cleanup

The number of labor hours being used varies greatly from one operation to another and from one segment of the foodservice industry to another.

**Exhibit 4.2 Example of a Typical Hospital Foodservice
Department in a Large Hospital in the 1980s**

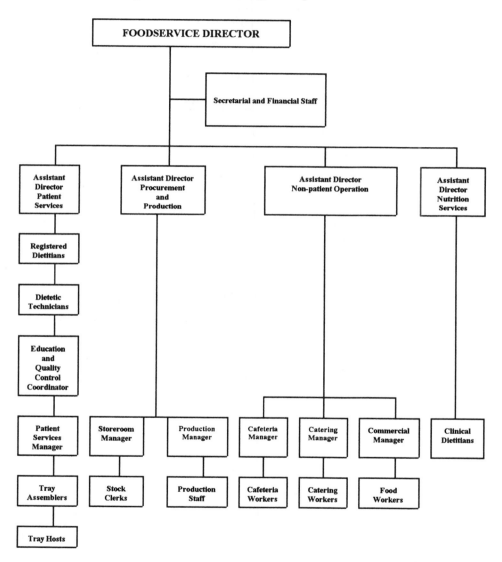

**Exhibit 4.3 Example of a Typical Hospital Foodservice
Department in a Large Hospital in the 1990s**

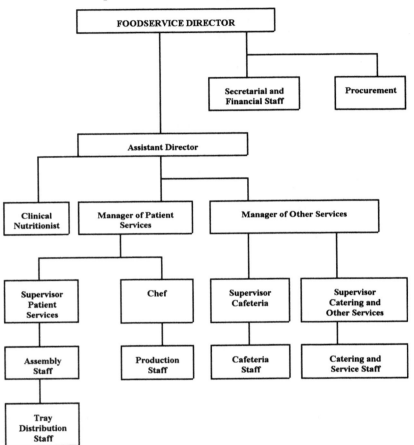

The health care foodservice staff has probably the most labor-intensive service of any of the foodservice industries. Most health care foodservice operators, for example, perform basically the same functions; however, several factors influence the staff needs, such as: size of facility, type of health care institution (acute care facility, standard hospital, or nursing home), types of food services offered (patient meal service, cafeteria, catering, etc.), and philosophy of management.

MEASURING PRODUCTIVITY

Measuring of productivity will become more of a management tool within the next few years as increasing productivity becomes important as a performance standard in the foodservice industry. Productivity increased overall in America in 1994, went down in 1995, and begin to climb by the end of 1996 through 1997. This trend will continue because directors/ managers are placing more importance on increasing productivity, and are tracking it.

Unfortunately, there is not one conceptual formula for determining the optimum number of labor hours needed to operate all segments of the foodservice industry. When one looks at what affects productivity, it is easy to see why a formula has not been developed. Exhibit 4.4 lists some of the factors that affect productivity.

How do we measure productivity? Productivity is the ratio of input to output. The formula is simply:

$\dfrac{\text{Output (Meals/Food and Service)}}{\text{Input (Labor Hours)}}$ = Productivity Rate

$\dfrac{\text{Number of Meals (or \$s)}}{\text{Number of Labor Hours}}$ = Productivity Rate
 or Meals per Labor Hour (MPLH)
 or Units of Service or Dollars in
                                                        Revenue

---

Exhibit 4.4 Factors Affecting Productivity of Foodservice Employees

- Type of food production system (e.g., on-site, most labor-intensive; or centralized commissary producing pre-plated meals, highest productivity)

- Level of service (e.g., made-to-order service, most labor- intensive; self-service, highest productivity)

- Number of meals served (e.g., the smaller the operation, the lower the productivity)

- Type of menu (e.g., set menu with limited choices, best productivity; extensive choices and changing menu, lowest productivity)

- Degree of prepared foods used (e.g., all selections made from raw ingredients or from "scratch," lowest productivity; total convenience foods, highest productivity)

- Type of equipment (e.g., manual work, lowest productivity; state-of-the art, automation, higher productivity)

- Efficiency of layout and design of kitchen and storage and service areas (e.g., facilities efficiently designed with good flow of foods from back door to service, high productivity)

- Size of facility (e.g., the smaller the operation, the lower the productivity)

- Type of dish washing system (e.g., use of disposables, higher productivity; heavy use of dishes, glassware, and silver, labor-intensive)

- Production planning and scheduling of employees (e.g., detailed written production plan with staff scheduled to arrive when work should begin, increased productivity over unplanned and unscheduled)

- Training and skill levels of employees (e.g., productivity increased when training in time and motion has taken place)

- Amount of supervision (e.g., supervision that is facilitating work, not looking over the employees' shoulders, improved productivity)

- Employee motivation (e.g., high employee morale and bonuses/rewards for meeting goals, increased productivity)

- Hours open for service (e.g., open for specific windows of time and closed during down time, improved productivity over open all day)

- Degree of computerization/automation used (e.g., everything possible computerized, increased productivity)

- Number of staff members and scheduling of their hours (e.g., optimum number, higher productivity; staff members scheduled when needed, higher productivity)

- Breaks (e.g., rest breaks after four hours of work, increased productivity)

Once the productivity rate has been determined, the next question to be answered is, how does management judge if productivity is high or low? Studies and surveys provide indicators of what is high productivity. These are frequently found in trade journals such as *Foodservice Director* and in studies by the National Restaurant Association. MECON Associates (San Ramon, CA) publishes an annual peer group analyses for the health care industry that is useful when evaluating financial and productivity data.

Determining Productivity Rates

The first step to calculating a productivity level in any industry is to determine what the "output" is and how to measure it. Output divided by input equals the "productivity rate." This sounds so simple. What is the output? Is it meals, in which case the question is, do all meals require the same amount of work? Should the output be measured in dollars of sales? Or is it best to measure productivity by the number of customers served? There are several ways of computing output, or productivity, and some of the most frequently used methods are described as follows:

- Number of transactions per labor hour

- Sales output per labor hour

- Meal equivalents produced and served or units of services per labor hour

- Percent of revenue for labor

- Number of covers (meals or customers) per labor hour

Number of Transactions per Labor Hour

In 1995 surveys by the trade journal *Foodservice Director* and by the National Restaurant Association showed that the number of transactions (customers served) varied greatly from one segment of the foodservice industry to another, as follows:

Hospital labor hour	= 4.8 transactions
Nursing home labor hour	= 3.5 transactions
College labor hour	= 10.1 transactions
School labor hour	= 17.0 transactions
B&I labor hour	= 14.0 transactions
Full-service restaurant average labor hour	= 8.4 transactions or covers
Fast-food restaurant labor hour	= 24.0 transactions
Cafeteria-type restaurant labor hour	= 10.0 transactions

The number of transactions (number served) per labor hour may be the best measure for schools, universities/colleges, cafeterias, hospitals (patient services), and nursing homes.

$$\frac{\text{Number of Customers}}{\text{Number of Labor Hours}} = \frac{\text{Number of Transactions}}{\text{per Labor Hour}}$$

Sales Output per Labor Hour

The restaurant industry frequently uses the dollar sales per labor hour for measuring productivity. According to surveys made in 1996 by *Foodservice Director* and by the National Restaurant Association, the average labor hour produced such varying dollar amounts that one should question if this is a reliable means of measuring productivity--maybe profitability (and isn't that what it's all about?) . Examples of the variances are as follows:

Hospital labor hour	= $ 19.11
Nursing home labor hour	= $ 11.88
College labor hour	= $ 15.67
School labor hour	= $ 21.57
B&I labor hour	= $ 21.57
Full-service restaurant labor hour	= $ 19.04
Fast-food restaurant labor hour	= $ 20.08
Commercial cafeteria-type restaurant labor hour	= $ 22.02

See Exhibit 4.5 for a summary.

The formula for determining the dollars in sales per labor hour is as follows:

$$\frac{\text{Dollars in Sales}}{\text{Number of Labor Hours}} \quad = \quad \text{Dollar Sales per Labor Hour}$$

According to the National Restaurant Association, in 1996 it took the equivalent of 12 full-time employees' work to generate $500,000 a year.

Exhibit 4.5 Measuring Productivity Per Labor Hour

Measurement	All	Hospital	Nursing Home	College	School	B&I	Small Rest.	Large Rest.
Transactions	8.4	2.7	3.4	7.9	12.5	5.6	6.9	8.4
Revenue Output	$18.97	$19.11	$11.88	$15.67	$21.57	$21.00	$19.04	$18.28
Hourly Salary	$9.82	$9.98	$8.85	$8.77	$10.26	$8.74	$9.35	$10.11
Payroll Cost per Transaction	$ 2.36	$ 7.08	$11.64	$1.58	$.81	$2.58	$1.73	$3.00
Average Transaction/ Customer	$ 1.61	$ 2.59	$ 4.47	$ 1.07	$.91	$2.40	$1.33	$1.95

Source: From *FoodService Director* " Productivity Study 1996." Copyright September 15,1997, by *FoodService Director*.

In Exhibit 4.5, the average transaction per customer of 91¢ in schools is the lowest in the foodservice industry. The 1995 survey indicated that B&Is had the highest salaries/labor costs in the industry, but B&Is dropped drastically in 1996. The 255 responders to the *FoodService Director* survey indicated that measuring productivity was much more important today than in the past as a management tool.

Meal Equivalents Produced and Served per Labor Hour

Meal equivalents produced in a labor hour are frequently used by school foodservices to measure productivity, and many school districts are using the guidelines in Exhibit 4.6 to staff individual schools. These districts are maintaining high productivity, and this means of determining how many hours to staff a foodservice has helped keep the labor costs in those districts with high productivity below 40% of the revenue. This is not high when you consider that meal charges are generally under $2.

When using meal equivalents, all types of sales are equated to a full meal--the work that goes into all types of sales is measured against the work that goes into preparing and serving a full meal. For example, the lunch is generally the main source of sales for schools. The breakfast meal is equated to the lunch using the method that two, three, or four breakfasts equal one lunch, or one meal equivalent. A la carte sales in dollars are equated to the lunch, and $3 to $4 in other sales, or the average check (in dollars), equals one lunch, or one meal equivalent.

Another method of determining a meal equivalent is based on the amount of work involved. The lunch and dinner meals may or may not be fairly equal with regard to the amount of work involved. Breakfast and "happy hour" in a restaurant cocktail lounge or bar involve less lengthy work. The following meal equivalents formula works for most foodservice operations.

1 lunch or 1 dinner	= 1 meal equivalent
2-4 breakfasts[1]	= 1 meal equivalent
Up to $3-$4[2] in a la carte sales	= 1 meal equivalent
or	
The average meal check[3]	= 1 meal equivalent

[1]Breakfast has a lower average check than lunch or dinner, but the amount of labor may not vary greatly. It depends on how much service is involved.

[2]Substitute average meal check here.

[3]The average meal check is arrived at by dividing total sales by the number of customers.

School districts with on-site preparation and high productivity average between 17 and 20 meals per labor hour. The foodservice operations on the West Coast have the highest productivity rates, and payrolls are the highest. University/college and public school management on the West Coast have been leaders in centralizing preparation, and this has resulted in increasing their productivity. High costs of wages and shortages of service employees have forced management to be more efficient, and this efficiency has contributed to the high productivity rates of on the West Coast. Schools on the West Coast also tend to use more student labor for short hours than schools located in other parts of the country.

The Hospital Administrative Services , an arm of the American Hospital Association, suggests that hospitals on a five-meal plan use 2.8 meals per patient day as a means of counting all the meals served to an inpatient. These calculations do not include tube feeding, nourishments, and infant formulas. Other means of evaluating the productivity are:

Number of minutes per patient tray
Number of minutes per non-patient meal
Number of transactions performed per employee (full time)

Another method of determining a meal equivalent factor is to determine the average customer check as the "output." Management companies often use this method because it provides more meal equivalents. The average daily sales at lunch (over a period of a month or several months) are divided by the average number of customers to determine the "average check." If total sales for the employee/guest cafeteria are $450 for lunch and an average of 150 customers are served, the average check is $450 \div 150 = $3, which represents sales per transaction or per customer.

$$\frac{\text{Number of Customers/Transactions}}{\text{Average Number of Labor Hours}} = \frac{\text{Number of Customers}}{\text{Per Labor Hour}}$$

Foodservice operations using cafeteria services may use the staffing guidelines in Exhibit 4.6 for determining the number of meals per labor hour that should be obtainable. For example, if the cafeteria (at a university, school, hospital, B&I) uses a lot of convenience foods and disposables and is serving approximately 200 breakfasts, 500 lunches, 550 dinners, and average $350 in extra sales a day, the meal equivalents (MEQ) are as follows:

200 Breakfasts ÷ 3	=	66 MEQ
300 Lunches ÷ 1	=	300 MEQ
350 Dinners ÷ 1	=	350 MEQ
$350 A la Carte ÷ $3	=	116 MEQ
		832 MEQ

832 MEQ   ÷   21 MPLH   =   39.62 or 39 3/4 labor hours

The guidelines in Exhibit 4.6 were used to determine at what productivity rate the cafeteria staff should function. If the cafeteria prepared a lot of food from raw ingredients and ran a dishwasher for most items, the MPLH at which the cafeteria would be staffed at is 18 (see Column 1 for MEQ and Column 2 for MPLH).

832 MEQ   ÷   18   =   46.22 or 46 1/4 labor hours

Exhibit 4.5 provides for a summary of measured productivity in various segments of the foodservice industry as reported in a productivity study conducted by the *Foodservice Director*.

Exhibit 4.6 Guidelines for Staffing Cafeterias for Production and Cafeteria-Type Service

NUMBER OF EQUIVALENTS[1] (1)	MEALS PER LABOR HOUR (MPLH)/TOTAL HOURS	
	CONVENTIONAL SYSTEM[2]	CONVENIENCE SYSTEM[3]
	MPLH (2)	MPLH (3)
Up to 100	8	9
101-150	9	10
151-200	10-11	12
201-250	12	14
251-300	13	15
301-400	14	16
401-500	14	18
501-600	15	18
601-700	16	19
701-800	17	20
801-1000	18	21
1001 up	20	23+

Adapted from: *Cost Control for School Food Service*, 2d Edition, by Dorothy Pannell-Martin. Copyright by inTEAM Associates, Inc., 1997.

---

[1]Meal equivalents include breakfast and a la carte sales. Three to four breakfasts equate to one lunch. A la carte sales of $3 to $4 equate to one meal equivalent.

[2]The conventional system is preparation of food from raw ingredients on the premises (using some bakery bread and prepared pizza and washing dishes).

[3]The convenience system is using the maximum amount of processed food (for example, all bakery breads, pre-portioned meals/poultry, and proportioned condiments), and using disposable dishes.

Percent of Revenue for Labor

Ratio analyses--determining the percentage of the revenue or sales spent on labor--provide a good means of evaluating how much is being spent for labor. The formula for obtaining the percentage is:

$$\frac{\text{Labor Costs}}{\text{Dollars in Sales}} \quad = \quad \text{Percentage of Revenue Spent for Labor}$$

Labor costs vary by geography, size of facility and operation, use of technology, and union/nonunion staffing patterns. The percent of revenue used for labor varies between 25 to 45 percent of the revenue. The lowest is in the fast-food restaurants, and the highest is in schools, health cares, and B&Is. The percentage of revenue spent on labor does not always reflect high or low productivity, but it may reflect salary levels and the amount of fringe benefits available to employees.

Breakfast tends to have lower checks (average amount of a sale), and the percentage of the revenue used for labor may be higher. However, the percentage of revenue spent for food should be less (lower).

STAFFING WITH JUST ENOUGH LABOR

How much labor is just enough? This is a question every manager needs an answer to. The most accurate way of setting the number of labor hours needed is to staff with a direct labor time analysis factor (DLTAF). To do this, work is planned and divided into 15-minute periods and is based on quantities of food to be prepared.

Good planning means having just enough labor scheduled when it is needed and no more than needed. This is possible when peaks and valleys are tracked and staffs are cross-trained, enabling one employee to do many different jobs.

There aren't many guidelines for staffing in the foodservice industry. Those that do exist are generally based on averages. Each location has its uniqueness, and only DLTAF allows for those uniquenesses but it involves maintaining a time log and charting the amount of time used for preparation, service, and cleanup. All is time-consuming and seldom done by small operations. It is certainly worth the effort if, for instance, a restaurant chain, several schools, several dining halls, or a number of employees can be involved.

The San Diego (CA) Unified School District Food Service Department staff has done some outstanding work analyzing the time it takes to do a job and the motions involved. They staff based on the jobs and how long each job takes. The staffing guidelines in Exhibit 4.6 have been tested against San Diego's DLTAF.

The type of production system, quantity to be prepared, and amount of convenience food used will influence greatly the number of hours needed. The method of production used can be divided into two major categories: on-site food production system and commissary/satellite production system.

On-Site Production

"On-site production" is a system of producing food and serving it on-site (same site). On-site production (and cooking with raw ingredients) requires more labor hours than any other system of producing food. Staffing of on-site production units often just happens. The staff can't do the work in the amount of time they presently have and thus more labor is added. Many managers have a budgeted amount they can spend on labor, or a percentage of revenue, and thus they have decided what will be spent on labor. Using budgeted amounts may not result in enough labor hours or too many labor hours to do the job. The large chain restaurants and management companies, e.g., Marriott, usually have staffing formulas they use.

The military has been successful in using staffing formulas. Staffing formulas may be used successfully in any type of operation where management has sufficient experience to establish the formula. The problem may be that management is ignoring the advantages of using a proven formula, or developing a formula.

Commissary/Satellite Production

Commissary/satellite production is a system of producing food for use at more than one site. " Commissaries" are locations at which food is produced in high volume/large quantities for more than one location and the food is transported to other locations to be served. When automation is used, this can be an efficient way of producing food.

Commissary preparation has been used by many small, and some large, chains. Many of the successful chain restaurants are using commissary preparation to increase productivity and lower the skill levels needed at the individual restaurant/service site. "*Sous vide*," a French term for "cooked in a vacuum," has gained in popularity among restaurants and hospitals using this procedure. With this method, individual portions of food as well as bulk products are prepared and bagged in heavy-duty plastic bags that can withstand temperatures at $180°+$ and at $-0°$. The food is transported to the place of service for reconstituting, e.g., Taco Bell.

The food may be transported in different stages, as follows:

Bulk cold- Food is cooked, chilled, or frozen and transported in bulk to other locations for service. This method is used effectively by some hospitals, schools, and correctional operations. The quality of the food can be excellent if food is cooked to its peak of perfection, and the cooking process is stopped by quickly bringing the temperature down in ice or ice water, or in a blast freezer. The productivity rate is increased by appropriately 20 percent when the volume is more than 3,000 meals and continues to climb with increased volume and automation.

Bulk hot— Food is prepared and transported hot in bulk quantities to other locations for service. This system is frequently used when there are no cooking facilities at the service area. Food quality and food safety are of utmost concern. This method is frequently used by schools and hospitals for service in an area without cooking or heating equipment.

Pre-plated cold (ready to eat)--Individual meals or parts of meals are prepared, pre-plated and cold and bagged or packaged, transported and served cold at another location, e.g., a bag lunch.

Pre-plated chilled or frozen--Individual meals are prepared, portioned, pre-plated chilled or frozen and transported, to be heated on-site for service. This method is used frequently by airlines and some intercity schools, e.g., Boston (MA) and Dayton (OH).

Pre-plated hot-- Meals are prepared, portioned, pre-plated, and transported hot to other sites usually involving short distances. This method has become very popular in the 1990s with carry-out food, e.g., Pizza Hut-delivered pizza.

Some locations receiving food have no cooking facilities and thus are limited to hot foods ready to eat. This is the best arrangement where the location has heating equipment. In such situations, the kitchens receiving mostly prepared foods from the commissary are known as <u>finishing kitchens</u>. This approach has been successfully used by many restaurant chains. Taco Bell has perfected this method, and thus the kitchen of a Taco Bell takes up 20 percent or less of the space and is able to maintain a 32 percent food cost. The final heating, reconstituting, portioning, and garnishing of food are done in the Taco Bell finishing kitchen at any location.

In many instances, foods are reconstituted (reheated) at the service location because the food does not travel well and is better cooked on-site in a finishing kitchen, e.g., french fries.

Using Staffing Guidelines

Staffing guidelines and comparison charts are especially useful to the new manager and for the seasoned manager to do a "self-check." See Exhibit 4.5 for a summary of productivity measurements. Exhibit 4.6 provides a guideline for on-site production with cafeteria-type service, Exhibit 4.7 for commissary production, and Exhibit 4.8 for finishing kitchen staffing with cafeteria service. An explanation of converting service to meal equivalents was discussed earlier in this chapter. The staffing guidelines for on-site production were explained earlier as well. Exhibit 4.9 provides an example of using the staffing guidelines for on-site production and for commissary production/finishing kitchens. Though these guidelines were developed originally by the author for a school foodservice operation, they are by no means limited to schools. Why shouldn't universities and colleges, B&Is, public dining rooms (cafeterias) in hospitals and correctional institutions, and even commercial cafeterias be able to obtain or exceed these productivity rates? Of course tradition, philosophy, physical setup, and other factors could make it impossible.

Exhibit 4.7 Sample Staffing Guideline for Commissary-Type Kitchen

NUMBER OF MEAL EQUIVALENTS (1)	MPLH AND NUMBER LABOR HOURS BY TYPE PREPARATION SYSTEM				
	BULK COLD[1] MPLH (2)	BULK HOT MPLH (3)	PRE-PLATED COLD (BAG)[2] MPLH (4)	PRE-PLATED FROZEN [1,2] MPLH (5)	PRE-PLATED HOT[2] MPLH (6)
200—500	25	27	21	22	20
501—1,000	30	30	30	37	40
1,001—2,000	50	45	50	55	60
2,001—3,000	65+	60	100	120	130
3,001—5,000	75+	70	110	120	130
5,001—10,000	130+	120	120	135	150
10,001—20,000	160+	130	130	135	150
20,000—30,000	175+	160	150	150	160
30,001 up	195+	175	150	175	190

Adapted from: *Cost Control for School Foodservice*, 2d Edition, by Dorothy Pannell-Martin. Copyright by inTEAM Associates, Inc., 1997.

Many commissaries provide parts of meals and other food items. It is easier to staff for meals than for individual items because so much depends on the complexity of the items. The question becomes ,"how long does it take to prepare the food?" A time study will help. Exhibit 4.7 can be used to staff a commissary-type kitchen producing items that are converted to meal equivalents. For example, if the equivalent of 2,500 MEQs are being produced at the commissary for bulk cook-chill (cold or frozen), the guideline recommends staffing at 60 MPLH, or 2,500 ÷ 60 = 41.66 labor hours.

---

[1]The labor hours of the driver who transports food should be figured into the hours allotted. The amount of time will depend on number of stops, distance, number and types of menus; however, the cost of delivering should be included in the total cost.

[2]Requires heating on site of service. Highly automated when over 2,000 food items are prepared.

Exhibit 4.8 Sample Staffing Guideline for Satellite/Finishing Kitchens with Cafeteria Service

NUMBER OF MEAL EQUIVALENT (1)	MPLH AND NUMBER OF LABOR HOURS BY TYPE PREPARATION SYSTEM				
	BULK COLD[1] (FK) MPLH (2)	BULK HOT[1] (FK) MPLH (3)	PRE-PLATED COLD (BAG) MPLH (4)	PRE-PLATED FROZEN[2] MPLH (5)	PRE-PLATED HOT MPLH (6)
Up to 75	16	17	75	30	50
76—100	18	19	75	30	50
101—200	20	21	100	50	75
201—300	22	24	100	60	75
301—400	26	26	100	60	75
401—500	26	28	100	60	75
501—700	28	30	100	60	75
701 up	30	32	100	60	75

Adapted from: *Cost Control for School Foodservice*, 2d Edition, by Dorothy Pannell-Martin. Copyright by inTEAM Associates, Inc., 1997.

The sites that receive the prepared food should be staffed for higher productivity than if the food were prepared on-site. For example, if the commissary delivers the equivalent of 525 bulk chill/cold meals to a "satellite" kitchen or deli or restaurant for heating, serving, and cleaning up after, the site receiving the food would be staffed (see Exhibit 4.8) at 30 MPLH or with 17 ½ labor hours. If the site has a combination of on-site (short order) production and heating/serving bulk chill/cold foods, the percentage of each would help to determine number of hours based on Exhibit 4.6 on-site and Exhibit 4.8 finishing kitchen.

[1]Meal equivalent of covers (meals).

[2]Needs heating.

Once the number of labor hours is decided upon, how will hours be used?

For example, at the on-site production site serving 832 MEQ with 39 3/4 labor hours, the hours would spread over the day. Ideally the work schedule would be planned first, then the number of people and hours for each would be determined. Management's hours are included in the 39 3/4 labor hours. The trend is toward one manager who works at peak hours and "lead" people who may open in the morning or close. This is illustrated below:

Open 7 a.m.

Breakfast Served   7:30 - 9:30
    "Prep" for lunch and dinner

Lunch Served   10:30 - 2:00
    "Prep" for dinner and tomorrow

Dinner Served   5:00 - 9:00

Close   10:00 p.m.

Jobs		Hours Scheduled	Total Number of Hours
Lead Person/	I	6:30 a.m. - 1:00 p.m.	6
Cashier	II	3:30 p.m. - 10:00 p.m.	6
Manager/Cashier		11:30 a.m. - 8:00 p.m.	8
Cook/Server	I	7:00 a.m. - 2:00 p.m.	6 ½
Cook/Server	II	11:30 a.m. - 8:00 p.m.	8
Cook/Server	III	4:30 p.m. - 9:00 p.m.	4
Sanitation and Cleanup*			1 ¼
TOTAL			39 ¾ hours

*Note: All employees will do a share of the cleaning all day and maintain high sanitation standards.

The number of hours assigned differs greatly among the different segments of the foodservice industry. Cafeteria-type services and many of the mid-range-price restaurants may use self-service and provide little or no service, whereas fine restaurants pride themselves in providing full service.

Exhibit 4.9 shows the actual staffing of ten self-operated on-site production health care foodservices. Based on the information provided ,the number of transactions per labor hour has been provided. The differences in productivity are interesting.

Exhibit 4.9 Staffing of 10 Self-Operated Health Care Foodservices

Facility (1)	Average Number Patients Fed/Day (2)	Average Patient Meal Cost per Day (3)	Equivalent Number of Full-Time Employees (4)	Average Daily Number Meals (5)	Number of Transactions Per Labor Hour (6)
Baptist Memorial Hospital Memphis, TN	700	NA	196	4,964	3.2
Beth Israel Medical Center New York, NY	750	$5.70	176	5,753	4.1
Henry Ford Hospital Detroit, MI	400	$5.70	147	3,205	2.7
University of California Sacramento, CA	293	$4.35	122	3,224	3.3
Laguna Honda Hospital San Francisco, CA	1,183	$4.89	111	4,121	4.6
St. Vincent Medical Center Little Rock, AR	1,092	$8.46	125	2,534	2.5
Carolinas Medical Center Charlotte, NC	524	$5.94	215	2,819	1.6
Cedars-Sinai Medical Center Los Angeles, CA	528	$8.43	183	5,048	3.5
The Medical Center at Univ. of CA, San Francisco, CA	395	$5.60	178	4,082	2.9
New York University Medical Center, New York, NY	785	$8.43	183	5,914	4.0

Source of data: *FoodService Director* Productivity Study of 1997 and Performance Report of 1996. Copyright by *FoodService Director* January 15, 1997, and September 15 , 1997. Column 6 was added to show productivity rates.

The service may take twice as much labor as the preparation. Exhibit 4.10 shows an example of how labor hours are used among different segments of the industry. It is interesting to note how similar all segments of the industry are with time spent on sanitation. Once work has been planned, it will be helpful to see how much time is set aside for each of the duties and particularly useful if there are a number of similar-type food units that can be compared.

Exhibit 4.10 Example of How the Foodservice Industry Uses Labor

Category	Administration Management	Service	Production	Sanitation
Full-Service Restaurants	22.5%	51.1%	25.0%	5.8%
Over $10	22.0%	32.0%	39.0%	9.0%
Under $10	20.9%	37.8%	37.1%	9.4%
Schools	10.0%	30.0%	51.0%	9.0%
Universities/ Colleges	10.0%	30.0%	51.0%	9.0%

Exhibit 4.11 provides the guidelines for staffing restaurants--the staffing standards are based on averages, and the labor hours for service will be greater the "finer" the restaurant. Exhibit 4.6 provides guidelines for cafeteria-style services. The school segment has one of the highest rates of productivity in preparation and service than any of other segments of the industry. The other segments can learn from them regarding how high their productivity can be.

Exhibit 4.11 Staffing Guidelines for Restaurants

Forecasted Covers*	Cooks: LH and C/LH	Dishwashers: LH and C/LH	Busboys: LH and C/LH	Servers: LH and C/LH	Total LH and C/LH
Breakfast 7-11 a.m.					
0 - 50	4.5 and 11.0	4.0 and 12.5	4.5 and 11.0	4.5 and 11.0	17.5 and 2.8**
51 - 100	4.5 and 22.0	4.0 and 25.0	4.5 and 22.0	8.0 and 12.5	21.0 and 4.7
101 - 150	5.5 and 27.0	4.0 and 37.5	4.5 and 33.3	10.0 and 15.0	24.0 and 6.25
Lunch 11 a.m.-4 p.m.					
0 - 50	5.0 and 10.0	5.0 and 10.0	5.0 and 10.0	8.0 and 6.25	23.0 and 2.1**
51 - 100	8.0 and 12.5	5.0 and 20.0	5.0 and 20.0	8.0 and 12.5	26.0 and 3.8
101 - 150	10.0 and 15.0	7.0 and 21.4	7.0 and 21.0	10.0 and 15.0	34.0 and 6.7
151 - 300	10.0 and 30.0	7.0 and 42.8	10.0 and 30.0	15.0 and 20.0	42.0 and 7.7
301 - 400	13.0 and 30.7	9.0 and 44.4	12.0 and 33.0	20.0 and 20.0	54.0 and 7.4
Dinner 4-10 p.m.					
0 - 50	6.5 and 7.6	6.5 and 7.6	6.5 and 7.6	13.0 and 3.8	32.5 and 1.5**
51 - 100	10.0 and 10.0	6.5 and 15.2	6.5 and 15.2	19.0 and 5.2	42.0 and 2.3
101 - 200	13.0 and 15.4	9.5 and 21.0	13.0 and 15.4	24.0 and 8.3	59.5 and 3.4
201 - 300	15.0 and 20.0	9.5 and 31.5	16.0 and 18.8	29.0 and 10.3	69.5 and 4.3
301 - 400	15.0 and 26.6	11.5 and 34.7	19.0 and 21.0	33.0 and 12.1	78.5 and 5.0

*Covers = Meals or Customers   LH =Labor Hours   C/LH = Covers per Labor Hour

**Fixed Labor Hours (Minimum Labor)

Source: *Fundamental Principles of Restaurant Cost Control* **by David V. Pavesic. Copyright 1998 by Simon & Schuster/Prentice-Hall, Inc.**

Exhibit 4.12 provides an example of staffing a restaurant. Note the staffing is for the peak days. Sunday through Wednesday will be staffed with fewer hours.

Hospitals have low productivity even in their non-patient cafeteria service areas. However, hospitals are having to change as budgets become tighter. Their cafeterias are comparable in many ways to public school and university cafeterias, where productivity is two to three times greater. According to Sneed and Dresse (1989), the hospital cafeteria services average 5.5 meals per labor hour. Exhibit 4.13 shows average and desirable meals per labor hour. Exhibit 4.6 provides guidelines for on-site production and service of a cafeteria that has been tested and that works.

Exhibit 4.12 Example of Staffing for a Restaurant Thursday Through Saturday[1] (Opened for Dinner Meal Only) With Average Revenue of $20,500 Per Day

POSITION (a)	NUM-BER (b)	TOTAL LABOR HOURS ©	% OF TOTAL LABOR (d)	AVER. WAGES PER LABOR HOUR (e)	FRINGE BENE-FITS (f)	TOTAL LABOR COST (g)	AVER. NO. CUS-TOMERS PER LABOR HOUR (h)	AVER. SALES PER LABOR HOURS (I)
Waitstaff	30	150	37.6%	$3.25	$ .65	$585.00	8	$136.66
Bus Staff	15	75	18.8%	$4.50	$ .90	67.50	16	273.33
Cooks	16	96	24.1%	$6.50	1.63	780.48	15	1,366.67
Hostesses	4	18	4.5%	$5.75	1.15	124.20	60	1,138.89
Cashiers	2	11	2.7%	$5.75	1.15	75.90	120	1,863.64
Bartenders	4	25	6.3%	$5.50	1.21	167.75	60	820.00
Sanitation Staff (Dish Washers)	4	24	6.0%	$5.50	1.20	160.80	60	820.00
TOTALS	75	399	100.0%	$5.25 (AV)	$1.127[2]	$5,961.63	14.1 (AV)	

AVERAGE COST $5,961.63 of LABOR/DAY + $20,500 SALE = 29.1% LABOR COST

a = job or position
b = number of employees
c = number of labor hours worked
d = labor hours in column c by position or divided by the total of all the labor hours in column c
e = average wages paid

f = fringe benefits (includes all costs)
g = labor cost (columns e + f) multiplied by number of labor hours
h = number of customers divided by number of labor hours
I = number of customers divided into total sales for average revenue

---

[1]Thursday-Saturday are peak days.

[2]The average costs do not include any leave days, e.g., paid vacation days or sick leave. If those costs exist, all costs should be included, e.g., FICA, Medicare, employees' meals, uniforms, laundry, etc.

Exhibit 4.13   Average and Desirable Meals per Labor Hour for Hospitals

Type of Service	Average Meals per Labor Hour	Desirable Meals per Labor Hour
Cafeteria	5.5	11-14
Acute Care Facility	3.5	5
Extended Care Facility	5.0	7

Some argue that a transaction is not a meal and it doesn't usually equal the amount of work involved in a meal. Measurement methods are important, and management needs to use the best measurement method. Some of the ways of measuring productivity are discussed below.

In cafeteria-type service, such as at a university, the productivity for a 2400-meal dining room may be 30 MPLH and the 80 labor hours (2400 ÷ 30 = 80). These hours may be divided as follows:

Production	60 percent	48 Hrs
Service	30 percent	24 Hrs
Management	10 percent	8 Hrs

A deli shop or small cafe may be staffed with or without a waitperson, based on whether or not it is self-service and how many customers a waitperson can adequately serve. A suggested staffing formula would be as follows:

Number of Customers	Number of Waitpersons
up to 30	1
31-60	2
61-90	3
91-120	4

FACTORS AFFECTING PRODUCTIVITY

Many factors affect the productivity of foodservice employees. Some of these factors are listed in Exhibit 4.4 and are discussed earlier in this chapter.

When employees are scheduled with a set amount of time to produce menu items, the productivity is generally greater than when there are no time lines. "Work expands to fill the time available" (Parkinson's law), particularly for unmotivated employees.

Not only should the productivity of the kitchen staff be measured, but scheduling, measuring, and increasing the productivity of the administrative staff can also save money. Productivity can be determined by recording the amount of time spent on each task. Then management can evaluate the cost of doing each task. Can the labor costs be afforded? Could an outside consultant perform the job in less time? These are questions being asked today. Contracting out a job may be cost-effective versus full-time employees performing the task on-site.

Harry Pope, who owned Pope Cafeterias in St. Louis, was a great exponent of creating a competitive attitude among the employees. He established a "score system" for measuring personal performances. This increased productivity considerably.

Employee Motivators

Rest Periods

There is no federal law requiring an employer to provide employees breaks, but several states do have laws regarding breaks after four hours of work. Some employers are allowing employees to eat meals on paid time instead of allowing "X" amount of time for a meal and adding the time to the length of the work day. The Fair Labor Standards Act (FLSA) does not address rest periods, coffee breaks, vacations, holidays, severance pay, or sick leave, and there are no differences in pay between weekends and weekdays.

Although FLSA does not address rest periods, coffee breaks, etc., labor union contracts, and some states and human resource departments have defined vacations, holidays, sick leave, and pay differential for weekends and night shifts.

Incentive Pay

The foodservice industry as a whole hasn't used incentive pay as much as some of the other industries. Motivating employees can be a challenge. Determining (1) what will motivate and (2) the criteria for providing incentive pay has to be the first step. The second step has to be determining what the incentive will cost and if it will be cost-effective.

One of the best examples of incentive pay that works is with the waitstaff, who depend on gratuities for most of their pay. A waitperson's pay is determined by how many they serve and the quality of that service, since over two-thirds of their pay is from tips. The waitperson is usually paid a "tipped" employee salary that is regulated by the FLSA. In 1997 it was based on 50% of the minimum wage per hour.

Performance-based incentives work, and for foodservice operations to remain competitive, management needs to use performance standards. Utilizing performance-based incentives or compensation is the trend in America today.

Some foodservice operations have found that providing an incentive such as new, attractive uniforms inspires pride and ownership of the program. Others have incentive programs in which employees earn awards for outstanding performance.

Berwick Hospital (PA) set a goal of serving all 500 residents in an hour. This became a motivator and resulted in successfully streamlining the tray line. Berwick also set up a separate service area for ambulatory residents (patients who can walk to a dining area). This received positive response from the patients.

The Jefferson County (KY) Schools foodservices has had in place a successful profit-sharing program for years. A staff of a school must agree to go with the profit-sharing program versus taking an annual raise. To share in the profits, the foodservice must achieve the established criteria, such as the customer count, and maintain a goal of low absenteeism rate, receive a sanitation score of 90 percent or higher, and make a profit. The reward can result in bonuses of up to $2,000 for each employee on the staff.

In a unionized environment, negotiated labor contracts discourage incentive or merit pay based on predetermined performance criteria. Union representatives prefer to negotiate a fixed rate of pay for all their employees.

However, employers should strive for at least part of the pay increases to be based on merit pay.

In restaurant chains, schools, universities with several dining halls, convenience stores, etc., an incentive program regarding level of pay can be effective. For example, a system of Lane I and Lane II pay scales could be used. Lane I is the base pay and if a staff accomplishes its (the foodservice's) goals for the year or half year, the employees would be promoted to Lane II, which pays slightly higher. If the staff failed to attain their goals following a period of time (year), their salaries would be frozen and not increased until the goals were met. Example of goals are:

- Established dollars in sales or number of customers served
- Sanitation score of 90 or higher
- Pre-set level of profits reached
- High attendance

Less Employee Turnover Rate

The foodservice industry overall has a high employee turnover rate--the highest being in fast-food restaurants (as high as 250% to 300%) and the lowest in schools (approximately 10%). High turnover reduces productivity because of the learning curve during the training period. In an effort to reduce the turnover rate, one fast-food establishment, McDonald's, provides incentives of points based on number of years worked, which can be turned into scholarship funds. To determine turnover rate, use the formula provided in Exhibit 4.14.

Exhibit 4.14.   Formula for Determining Turnover Rate

Number of Employees Who Quit or Are Fired
Total Number of Employees   =   Turnover Rate

Example: If 10 employees leave positions and there is a total of 40 employees remaining, the turnover rate is:

  10 Employees Departed   =   25% Turnover Rate
  40 Employees

Some segments of the industry, e.g., schools, hospitals, and self-operated B&Is, have suffered from low turnover rates and an older work force who may be slower. This can mean lower productivity and more accidents.

Scheduling

Staffing and scheduling are both important to high productivity; however, probably the number one factor to be considered in achieving high productivity is scheduling--(1) when a person comes to work and leaves work, and (2) the time allotted for each job. Staffing designates number of workers; scheduling designates who will do the job, and when, what, and where. Consider the following when scheduling:

- Staggering arrivals and departures
- Using flexible scheduling
- Using split shifts if employees will work them
- Using overtime occasionally
- Using part-time employees for days when need is the greatest
- Cross-training and using employees in different positions

High productivity and low labor costs will result when labor is used effectively and is controlled by scheduling employees efficiently. The volume of business or size of the operation and preparation to be done should determine when employees are scheduled to work. The volume of business according to the days of the week, the season of the year, and the hours of the days are all factors to consider when scheduling an employee's hours of work.

Ideally, management should plan and schedule the work first, then establish the employees' work time. The foodservice manager should start by first planning and scheduling work in 15-minute blocks. To determine how long it should take to do a task, a stop-watch should be used to measure the time required to do the task (see Exhibit 4.15 for an example). Then the quantity of work the employee should be able to complete in a given period of time should be determined and expressed in a format that employees can follow (see example of a sample work schedule in Exhibit 4.16).

Labor and work (jobs) scheduling can be time-consuming and complex. Marriott Management Services is using a labor-scheduling software program to maximize labor and increase productivity by 8.3% in the management services division. They have cut labor costs by $2 million in two years. They are using software in B&Is, in 70% of their health care accounts, and in all their Canadian operations.

The written work scheduling, coupled with team training, and cross-training, will help ensure even greater productivity for management companies and for self-operated facilities.

Century Management used in the past an empowered team-based approach to improving work processes, service, and unit productivity. It was a motivator that paid off with increasing productivity.

Aramark, a Philadelphia-based management company, has put into place an eight-step "Spirit of Service" training program that teaches how to serve customers more quickly and more pleasantly, and also a "back-of-the house" training program for the cooks and kitchen staff to encourage more meals per labor hour.

Exhibit 4.15 Time Required to Perform Task

Task and Quantities Produced	Time Required
Cut watermelon, 100 servings	20 minutes
Pan hamburger patties, 120	12 minutes
Assemble/wrap hamburgers, 120	15 minutes
Prepare and cut peanut butter/ jelly sandwiches, 100	25 minutes
Assemble (18" x 26") pizzas, 1 topping, 72 portions	8 minutes
Assemble soft tacos, 10 dozen	20 minutes
Assemble ham and cheese sandwiches, 10 dozen	20 minutes
Frost sheet cake, 1	1 minute
Prepare pans and pan brownies, 1	2 minutes
Prepare pans and pan cookies, 192	15 minutes
Bag french fries, 120	30 minutes

Source: *Work Methods* **by Yvette Major, labor management specialist, San Diego Unified Schools, Food Service Department, n.d**.

Exhibit 4.16 is an example of a sample work schedule in 15-minute intervals. A few basic steps to planning a work schedule are:

- Plan work first, then assign people.

- Divide work into 15-minute intervals; plan reasonable amounts of work to be completed within the time.

- Start by penciling in peak service times (times when jobs must be filled, e.g., meal time).

- Schedule employee breaks.

- Determine the time the employee should start and stop based on the job to be done.

Exhibit 4.16   Sample Work Schedule for B&I or School

MENU - BREAKFAST	inTEAM Food System	MENU - LUNCH
Cinnamon Rolls (2) - Blueberry Muffins (2) French Toast (2) - Sausage (2) Cereal - Toast (2) Toast (2) - Sausage (2)	**WORK SCHEDULE** (To be completed for each day of each menu cycle)	Spaghetti/Meat Sauce - Garlic French Bread Chef Salad/Egg and Cheese - French Bread Spaghetti with Meat Sauce Taco with Meat/Bean and Cheese Tossed Salad/Dressing, Applesauce, Fruit Sherbet

TUESDAY - WEEK 1

POSITION	1 MANAGER	2	3
NUMBER HOURS	7	6	6
7:00 - 7:15	Unlock; pick up change fund; count. Prepare computer for breakfast..	Set out cereal and set up milk in cooler. Put cinnamon rolls and blueberry muffins in heated cabinet.	
7:15 - 7:30	Set out trays, napkins, and sporks.	Prepare sausage and toast.	
7:30 - 7:45	Set out juice, fruit, and trail mix.	Prepare French toast.	
7:45 - 8:00	Set up serving line with hot food.		
8:00 - 8:15	Cashier on the line.	Serve breakfast.	Prepare lettuce for tossed salad. Slice cucumbers and shred carrots for chef salad. Shred cheese for week's menu. Dice tomatoes for tacos. Cook eggs for chef salad.
8:15 - 8:30			
8:30 - 8:45	Count breakfast money. Complete breakfast production record.	Put away breakfast. Clean serving line. Clean tables.	
8:45 - 9:00	Set up juice and fruit cup.[1] Label breakfast and refrigerate.	Pan sliced ham; cover with plastic bag and refrigerate[1] Prepare egg mixture for Wednesday[1]	Wrap and pan apple cinnamon muffins, coffee cake, and English muffins in pan to be served in. Cover with plastic and refrigerate. Label[1]
9:00 - 9:15	Set up 10 cereals. Set up fruit cup[1]	Portion shredded cheese. Prepare garlic bread. Prepare spaghetti and meat sauce. Prepare meat and beans for tacos.	
9:15 - 9:30	Prepare computer and money for cashier.		Prepare chef salads.
9:30 - 10:00	Portion applesauce. Mix tossed salad and portion.		
10:00 - 10:15	**EAT LUNCH**		
10:15 - 10:30		**EAT LUNCH**	Portion croutons. Wash pots and pans.
10:30 - 10:45	Wash fresh fruit and display. Place utensils and condiments on serving line.		
10:45 - 11:00		Set up steam table. Check temperatures of food and steam table.	

[1]Next day's breakfast items.

Exhibit 4.16 Sample Work Schedule for B& I or School (continued)

	LUNCH 11:00 - 1:00		
11:00 - 11:15	**LUNCH** Check line; batch cook; keep food on line. Backup serving line. Observe and communicate with customers. Portion more fruits and fixings as needed.	**LUNCH** **Serve on line** (Wash pots and pans during break in service).	**LUNCH** Cashier on line. Serve on line. Spot check line for cleanliness, debris on floor, and condiments needing replacement.
11:15 - 11:30			
11:30 - 11:45			
11:45 - 12:00			
12:00 - 12:15	Supervise money counting. Determine food used for first hour.		
12:15 - 12:30	Back up serving line.		
12:30 - 12:45	Back up serving line.		
12:45 - 1:00		Count food left/portions-- record.	
1:00 - 1:15	Supervise money counting. Close out computer.	Record and store leftovers. Clean serving line. Cart canned items to be used following day. Check for following day's items.	Count money. Prepare reconciliation form.
1:15 - 1:30	Determine food used for second hour. Check production record for food usage. Adjust next day's record for leftovers. Complete production record.		**EAT LUNCH**
1:30 - 1:45			
1:45 - 2:00			Wash pots and pans. Wipe tables and seats. Store food in storeroom. Clean storeroom.
2:00 - 2:15	Check cleanup.		
2:15 - 2:30	Complete final preparation for next day; check		

Source: *Manager's Production Handbook* by Dorothy Pannell-Martin, Gertrude Applebaum, and Elizabeth Soares. **Copyright 1998 by inTEAM Associates, Inc.**

AVERAGE COST OF A LABOR HOUR

The "real," full cost of a labor hour is not limited to what is paid the employee in salaries and wages. The real cost includes all costs related to employees. The September 1997 issue of the *Foodservice Director*, a widely read foodservice periodical, reported the average cost of labor per week and per hour as shown in Exhibit 4.17. These rates do not include fringe benefits, which would increase these rates 12 to 40 percent depending upon the benefits provided.

Exhibit 4.17 Average Costs of Weekly and Hourly Labor Hour[1]

	Hospital	Nursing Home	College	School	B&I	Average
Average Weekly Foodservice Pay	$307.50	$270.10	$225.40	$196.66	$349.79	$283.50
Average Hourly Foodservice Pay	$ 9.70	$ 8.93	$ 8.87	$ 7.81	$ 17.16	$ 9.93

Source: *FoodService Director 1996 Productivity.* Copyright September 15, 1997, by *FoodService Director.*

The average labor costs vary greatly, as shown in Exhibit 4.17. Self-operated B&I salaries appear to be way out of line as compared to labor costs in other segments of the foodservice industry.

The average cost of a labor hour in the foodservice industry is higher in the western states. For example, in 1995 the average worker's hourly salary in the west was $10.48 (including fringe benefits) compared to $9.93 for the foodservice industry as a whole. This average is figured on the days worked, not the days paid. This average cost of a labor hour is even greater when figured based on the total amount paid divided by the hours the employee has actually contributed toward generating revenue or sales. For example, the employee in a hospital foodservice may have two weeks of paid vacation,

---

[1]This reflects cost of an hour worked, which includes the costs of fringe benefits including sick leave days, paid holidays, and vacation days. For example, the hourly wages in 1997 for foodservice employees was $7.69 in hospitals; nursing homes, $6.72; colleges/ universities, $5.63; schools, $4.92; and B&Is, $8.74; the average hourly wages were $6.74.

five paid holidays, and ten paid sick days a year. These fringe benefits add to the costs of an hour actually worked. The real question is, how much does an hour of work cost? Exhibit 4.18 shows the average costs of an hour of work.

The prisons using inmates for labor may appear to have low labor costs but this is not always true. According to Jerry Collins, the national foodservice administrator of the Federal Bureau of Prisons, federal penal institutions are paying supervisory staff up to $16 an hour. Inmate labor provides a lot of the work and seemingly is cheap, costing 12¢ to 38¢ per hour (depending on the inmate's dependability and skills), but the supervision at $16 per hour is costly, and the inmates require close supervision.

The highest labor costs will often be found in self-operated foodservices. Twenty-five percent of the labor cost may be fringe benefits in some of these foodservices; but fringe benefits can be as high as 40 percent in business and industry self-operated foodservices. Exhibit 4.18 provides the steps to figuring the real cost of a productive labor hour. This exhibit shows all labor costs, including fringe benefits.

Exhibit 4.18   Average Cost of Productive Hour of Work

The average cost of productive work is very different from the hourly wage or salaries paid. Included in the following are all salaries and fringe benefits for employees working in foodservices (including hostesses, cashiers, dishwashers, etc.). The only salary not included is that of the manager.

1. Add together all salaries and wages for one year.
2. Add all fringe benefits (employer-paid taxes, worker's compensation, health insurance, free meals, uniforms, laundry of uniforms, etc.)
3. Add all substitute pay (for substitutes used to replace employees on paid leave) for one year.
4. Divide total of 1, 2, and 3 by number of days the foodservice is operated in the year.

The answer is the **average cost of labor per day.**

5. Divide the average cost of labor per day by the total number of labor hours on a typical day.

The answer is **the average cost of a labor hour.**

6. To determine the labor cost per customer, divide the annual cost (total of 1,2, and 3 above) by the total number of customers a year. Or, divide the cost of labor per day by the average number of customers served per day.

The answer is **the average cost of serving a customer.**

Management in most segments of the industry will argue that a productive hour is equal to an hour worked (total salaries and benefits are equal to hours paid). The hidden costs are sick leave, holiday pay, breaks, and vacation days. If the cost of labor is added together for a year and divided by the actual hours the employees work in which people are served, the costs are usually higher than one expects.

Studies have shown that foodservice employees are really productive only 50 percent of the time because much of the time is spent walking, watching, and doing unnecessary work. If this is true, then the cost of a productive labor hour is twice the cost computed in step 6 above. Exhibit 4.19 provides an example.

Exhibit 4.19 Example of Cost of a Productive Hour of Work in a Small Commercial Restaurant

1. Total Salaries of Wages for All Foodservice Employees (except management) for Year, to Include Sick Days, Vacations, and Holidays	$	101,829
2 Fringe Benefits (Employer's Share) for Year		
Social Security	$	7,962
Health Insurance		15,795
Life Insurance		104
Retirement/IRA		9,892
Worker's Compensation		3,011
Unemployment Insurance		62
Employee Meals		936
Uniforms		1,500
Laundry of Uniforms		2,340
Total Cost of Fringe Benefits for Year	$	41,602
3. Substitutes' Wages for Year		6,158
4. Total Labor Costs for Year	$	149,589
5. Number of Days in Operation 362	$	149,589
6. Divide Total Labor Cost for Year(#4) by Number of Days of Operation (#5), which gives the Average Daily Labor Cost		÷ 362 = $ 413.23 per day
7. Divide Daily Labor Cost by Average Number of Labor Hours = Average Cost of a Labor Hour	$	413.23 ÷ 33 hrs = $ 12.53 per hour
8. Divide the Average Cost of a Labor Hour, #7, (based on a 50% productivity rate) by 2 = Average Cost of a Productive Labor Hour	$	25.04

When salary increases are not based on merit, but rather are "automatic" increases, an operation can price itself out of business by giving poor quality service at high prices. Corrective action to discontinue the automatic increases may be needed. A comparison of the wages paid by a foodservice in the same community doing similar work can be useful. How much does the foodservice industry in your city or state pay labor? The National Restaurant Association publishes annual average labor costs by state and region, and nationwide. The survey results is made up of data submitted by the local state restaurant associations. Exhibit 4.1 shows national averages in 1997, but it needs to be updated annually with local data for the information to be relevant, particularly in light of the new minimum wage laws and their effects on the foodservice industry.

REDUCING LABOR HOURS AND COSTS

The trend of reducing the size of the workforce in most industries started about 1994, when the workplace became 14% smaller than in 1993. The predicted shortages in the early 2000s in service employees (especially foodservices) may be taken care of if this trend of increasing productivity continues.

The hospital segment has had to be the most creative over the last three years as they have seen their customer base dwindle. Most hospitals today have 30% to 35% fewer labor hours on their foodservice payrolls than they did in 1993. In some cases the cuts have resulted in no backup for absent employees.

Studies done by Penn State University show that a reduction in the foodservice labor force will automatically happen in the next five years due to attrition. Between now and the year 2000, four out of ten of the foodservice industry's "most experienced operators" will retire or leave the field. The biggest loss is expected in B&I, with a 68% loss, then prisons, with 47%; and schools, with 44% .

When the productivity rates of the different segments of the foodservice industry are compared, it is easy to see that cafeteria or self-service feeding gets much higher productivity than sit-down service. The effects of minimum-wage increases, low unemployment rates, and the shortage of a trained labor force are making it essential for all segments of the foodservice industry to look at ways of improving productivity and decreasing the need for labor .

A number of ways to reduce labor hours and the costs of a labor hour are addressed on the following pages.

Standardizing and Simplifying System of Operation

Standardizing and simplifying the entire operation has proven successful for many nationwide chains and systems of management, e.g., Olive Garden restaurants, the school districts using the inTEAM Food System, and Morrison's Management Company. The secret of success has been streamlining the system of operation and using short menu cycles, as done by Morrison's Management Company and school districts using the inTEAM Food System, and the repeated limited menus done by Olive Garden. The standardization of the process--menus, recipes, and atmospheres--has resulted in efficient use of labor and reduced labor costs, and improved quality.

HC   The Integris Southwest Medical Center in Oklahoma City, a 280-bed facility, has reduced labor costs (as well as printing costs) by planning and distributing weekly menus instead of daily menus. This approach can be extended to a two- or three-week menu cycle. The weekly menus are kept in a binder on every patient's bedside table. No longer do menus have to be delivered and collected daily--eliminating the need for nurses and staff to deliver and pick up menus. This can work in long-term care facilities.

In most hospitals, 3-5 day stays are considered "long," and diets may change once or twice during the day. In these cases, the interactive TV has the potential of enabling patients to select their menus, particularly as the general public becomes more computer-literate.

One of the secrets to McDonald's early success was the 10 menu items. Today the offering of more than 50 items has complicated the process and has taken its toll on quality and speed at McDonald's and other fast-food restaurants who have increased menu selections. However, customers demand menu variety, value, and service. Responding to the customer demands is called being attentive to "customer satisfaction," and without that a company/foodservice loses customers to the competition.

Centralizing Management and/or Preparation

Centralizing management and/or preparation or both reduces middle management and results in one person managing several units or activities. The trend is toward more multi-department managers, e.g., catering manager and cafeteria manager being one and the same.

Commissary-type operations and centralized preparation in one unit providing food for other units will often reduce the total cost of labor, especially the need for skilled employees. Many chain restaurants and management companies utilize the centralized preparation concept to reduce costs.

Many chain restaurants (small and large) and foodservices in universities/colleges, hospitals, B&Is, and school districts utilize centralized preparation to keep labor costs down. Cook-chill is used in all segments of the foodservice industry and has proven cost-effective for many. Cook-chill or cook-freeze is one of the best means of producing food in volume for service elsewhere later. Cook-chill not only can increase productivity but also can reduce the skill levels of employees needed. Expertise is needed for producing the product but not later at the location where the food will be heated and served. The quality will be as good as when it was produced at peak. Cook-chill/cook-freeze reduces the number of employees needed and allows labor to be "stored up" labor in ready-to-heat-and-serve food.

"*Sous vide*" is a form of cook-chill/cook-freeze that is being used by many hospitals and restaurants. Individual servings are cooked and packaged in vacuum-sealed pouches for future use. Many expensive cook-chill kitchens have been built in the last 10 years but have often sat idle several hours a day or several days of the week. Thus the most cost-effective way of using cook-chill food preparation may be to purchase the food from a commercial kitchen.

Townsend Culinary, Incorporated (formerly Grace Culinary Kitchen), a commercial cook-chill kitchen located in Laurel, Maryland, prepares *sous vide*, as well as bulk foods (cook-chill/cook-frozen), to be used in a variety of foodservice operations. Their expert chefs use the clients' recipes and run the pathological tests for bacteria count prior to shipping the food out. Some gourmet *sous vide* foods are going to popular upscale chains of white-tablecloth restaurants; also, *sous vide* has a place in hospitals/nursing homes. Though this process was developed and used in Europe many years ago, it has been perfected at plants that specialize in the process in this country, like Townsend Culinary, Incorporated.

B&I   Oracle Corporation's B&I facilities are using the commissary to prepare cold sandwiches, and the commissary staff has the potential of preparing other items. Centralizing the preparation of some items has reduced Oracle Corporation's and others' labor costs.

The use of the centralized ingredient room, popular in the 1950s and 1970s, is being re-instituted by some segments of the foodservice industry. The ingredient room use has resulted in reduced labor costs, better quality and quantity control, lower food costs, and, often, improved quality. To accomplish the ingredient room procedures, one or two people weigh out all the ingredients for every recipe and provide the ingredients to the work station in the appropriate amounts and at the appropriate time. Several foodservice texts provide details for setting up quality and quantity control stations, such as the inTEAM *Food System Manual for Administrators*.

RES   Charles Horan, who formerly managed Colonial Cafeterias in Fort Worth, encouraged unit managers to compare their productivity with that of similar units. This competition resulted in greater productivity.

Sharing Services

Labor costs can be reduced substantially by sharing professional and managerial expertise in a hospital, B&I operation, university, or school with other departments in the hospital, company, or university, school or with other facilities, whereby each department or facility has highly trained personnel on a part-time basis. For example, food and supply purchasing can be done in a cooperative arrangement with several different departments or facilities paying the salary of the person or group doing the purchasing.

Some of the full-service management companies, e.g., Aramark and Marriott, have reduced administrative labor costs by contracting to provide more than foodservices for a customer, e.g., maintenance and cleaning services. These companies also have one person in charge overall with an operations manager for foodservice and one for custodial services.

A few directors/managers in hospitals and schools have taken over more than one operation, e.g., the Cleveland County (NC) foodservice director provides custodial services to the school district. This has reduced upper management costs.

Using Convenience Foods

A "kitchenless kitchen" was first used by St. Louis City Schools and later by Cedars-Sinai Medical Center (Los Angeles, CA), then later by many others. With the improved quality of frozen foods and the wide variety available, it is possible for a full menu to be put together from components that are ready to heat and serve. The labor costs are in the price of the food, and when the automated processors have maintained high productivity the costs have been less than preparing on-site. In the long run the use of convenience foods can reduce food costs because of better portion control and no preparation waste involved. The number of items in inventory is kept lower, portion control is improved, and in turn food cost is lowered. Labor costs should be very low.

Frozen doughs are practical in many situations. They are used almost exclusively in the larger grocery store bakery outlets.

Exhibit 4.20 shows the comparison between costs of using frozen cinnamon roll dough and ready-to-eat roll, and of preparing the roll from raw ingredients. The quality control is probably more effective when prepared at the food processing company.

Exhibit 4.20 Comparison of Convenience Foods and Cooking from Raw Ingredients

Cinnamon Rolls -- Made from "Scratch"[1]	Cost per Portion/Roll (2 oz)
Ingredients------------------------------------- $.04 2 Hours of Labor @ $8.00--------------------- .16	$ .20/Roll
Cinnamon Rolls -- Using Convenience Foods[1]	
Frozen Dough --------------------------------$ .082 1 Hour of Labor @ $8.00 -------------------- .08	$ .162/Roll
Cinnamon Rolls -- Purchased Ready-to-Serve	
Ready-to-Serve Roll	$ .33/Roll

The question often asked is, "Should one use convenience food or make food from scratch?" The answer will depend on what the best, most cost-effective way is.

Assemble-and-serve food production (or use of total convenience foods) results in a system that requires minimal use of skilled labor. These systems can foster efficient use of labor, which may be the only way to quickly reduce labor costs where unions controls are strong.

Unfortunately, most operations gradually increase their use of convenience foods and yet do not realize the labor savings that should come with it. If the convenience foods are added gradually, Parkinson's Law, "Work expands to fill the time available," takes over. If the implementing of the convenience food system can be planned, and if a changeover to using a convenience food system is done all at one time, savings should be realized. If the average cost of a productive labor hour is running more than $10, one should begin looking at ways to decrease the costs. Before taking this drastic

---

[1]A good aroma is realized with this method as well as with preparing from raw ingredients, and the aroma is important to attracting customers, particularly in a foodservice in a shopping mall food court, school cafeteria, B&I facility and hospital.

step, one should consider the pluses and minuses and be sure the following are true:

- Products meet the nutritional standards and modified diets.

- There is enough variety to make an acceptable menu cycle.

- Quality standards and customer acceptability are high.

- Cost per serving is in the acceptable range.

- Refrigeration space will accommodate changes.

- Labor hours can be reduced to realize a savings and offset higher food costs.

- Waste disposal of containers will not be a problem.

Training and Cross-Training

Reducing labor hours will not automatically cause employees to be more productive. However, if hours are to be reduced, the productivity of the remaining staff has to be increased. This will take training in work simplification practices and time and motion conservation. Ongoing training in work simplification practices and "working smarter" should be established by management. Working smarter means eliminating the unnecessary and using the best methods.

Colleges/universities, schools, B&Is, and health care facilities are developing integrated service teams whereby an employee is cross-trained in more than one service area. For example, combining services is being used, and an employee may work for more than one department. The cross-training in some health care units focuses on the entire facility. An employee will work in foodservices at the peaks of service when the needs are the greatest, then in another department when not needed in foodservices. This use of an employee in more than one job has reduced labor costs in many foodservice operations. For example, in a hotel the doorman may also work as maître d', and in health care units, passing out food trays could be assigned to new employees or guest service representatives.

Participating in Work-Training Programs

Participating in work-training programs can benefit both the employer and the employee. It usually means the employer obtains labor at a reduced or subsidized rate, such as in the government work programs and in the culinary schools' apprenticeship-type programs. These programs provide management the opportunity to better train the employees at reduced costs and the employees (apprentices) the opportunity to obtain experience in the real world.

Tax Breaks for Work Programs--Under the new federal government efforts to get people off welfare, many dollars in tax breaks are available to the foodservice industry to train people for employment. Though such programs require management to organize and structure the work experience, the payoff is less expensive labor and an opportunity to train potential employees before they go on the payroll. In 1997-98 the employer could claim a 35% tax credit on the first $6,000 of wages paid to eligible workers (35% of the first $3,000 of wages paid to a summer-youth employee). The employee must work at least 180 days or 400 hours during the regular season for the employer to obtain the tax break.

Internships with Culinary Schools--Young potential chefs from the culinary schools make good, enthusiastic employees. Their pay is less than for a full-time chef and the energy level is usually high. The training work programs are somewhat like a school-to-work or an apprenticeship-type job.

Apprenticeship-type jobs, or job-experience-type programs provide on-the-job training that benefits the employee and the employer. The employer is also playing a part in the community and giving back to the industry.

Using Part-Time Workers

One of the biggest advantages of using part-time workers or substitutes cost-wise is in fringe benefit savings. For example, part-time employees generally are paid only for the hours worked and basic employer taxes. They are not paid sick leave, health insurance benefits, or vacation leave. The difference in the cost of a labor hour of a part-time worker and the full-time worker with benefits can be considerable.

SCH   In one large school district a part-time employee who works less than four hours does not cost the employer as much per hour as does a "full-time" employee who works four hours or more. The part-time employee does not receive some of the same benefits. The full-time employee who works four hours a day is costing $10.80 per hour (starting salary), receives a 15-minute break, and is entitled to health care benefits. The part-time employee is costing $8.76 per hour (starting salary). The cost of 30 minutes more in a day (15 minutes more of work time) is shown in Exhibit 4.21.

Exhibit 4.21 Cost Comparison of Part-Time Versus Full-Time Employee

Employee	Wages	Break	Health Insurance	Cost of a Labor Hour[1]	Cost of Labor for a Day
Part-Time Employee, 3 ½ hrs[2]	$ 7.97	NA	NA	$ 8.76	$30.66/ 3 ½ hrs of work time
Full-Time Employee, 4 hrs[3]	$7.97	15 minutes	YES	$10.80	$43.20/ 3 3/4 hrs of work time

Fifteen more minutes of work time costs $12.54.

---

[1]Cost of labor hour includes employer taxes on employee.
[2]Part-time employee may work 3 ½ hours or less.
[3]Full-time employee may work from 4 hours to 8 hours per day.

Changing and Expanding Services

Changing services or expanding services should be done based on need and evidence of a need. When sales are tracked, management can analyze what makes up the sales and when the sales occur. For example, it may not make sense to be open on Monday evenings or seven days a week. What made up sales five years ago may have changed drastically over the five years. For example, the traditional daily specials may not be cost-effective and may need to be replaced with different types of specials.

Increasing Self-Service

Self-service bars are on the increase. For example, colleges and universities are making pizza stations self-service. Deli bars, salad bars, and yogurt bars with toppings are self-service operations and are priced by the pound/ounce. This type of service is often a favorite with customers and reduces labor costs substantially.

Using Cart Service

HC   Cart service has eliminated the tray assembly for breakfast in some hospitals and has improved the satisfaction levels. Wine and cheese carts in the afternoon at a private, upscale nursing home have been a popular addition. Cart service has potential for B&Is and hospitals/nursing homes for visitors, for universities for faculty and administration, and for some restaurants/ bakeries. The airlines haven't used this type of service enough as a means of delivering food and increasing customer satisfaction.

HC   The New York University Medical Center has streamlined delivery of breakfast on carts, saving $175,000 and receiving positive feedback from customers. This 840-bed facility offers upscale menu items, e.g., broiled salmon, fresh fruit juices, and home-baked muffins. The wide selection of food is served right in front of the patient on disposable dishes and with disposable wares. This has reduced staff time for assembling, retrieving, and washing of trays.

HC   The St. Joseph Hospital (Denver), a 565-bed facility, has revamped an outdated tray assembly system and introduced a "closed-cart system," where the cart goes from hospital room to hospital room for selections to be made. It has reduced labor costs, improved customer satisfaction, and saved $26,000 on lids and covers.

SCH
U/C
Schools, universities, and colleges are using carts to expand the number of service areas and capture customer sales they may have otherwise lost. One school district reported a 500% increase in breakfast sales when the foodservice staff made the breakfast foods easy-to-eat items, put them on a cart, and wheeled them to the front entrance of the school or the middle of the lecture hall in the university.

Expanding Services

HC
The Knox Community Hospital (OH), a 115-bed facility, has expanded its services to take up the slack from reduced numbers of patient meals by providing "Meals on Wheels" for volunteers to deliver in the community. Catering meals and providing carry-out foods have become major sources of income as well.

SCH
Dayton City (OH) Schools' central commissary produces meals for all the district's schools, as well as community day cares, senior citizen programs, private schools, and other smaller public schools.

Maximizing Time Open for Service

Maximizing time open for service by reducing hours/days to the most profitable times may reduce revenue, but if cost is not reduced more than revenue, it can result in a savings. When maximizing the time open, the customer count needs to be tracked and facilities closed on real down times or days, e.g., at universities/colleges close the grill at breakfast on weekends and possibly at lunch and dinner on Sunday. Also, shorter service time or consolidate service in limited stations can reduce costs. Vending of more entrees, sandwiches, and salads, can provide what could be used to make a meal at the off hours or when dining services are not open.

U/C
The University of California at San Diego is considering many options for lowering its costs in order to provide funds for new facilities. Management is considering reducing the hours open from 7 a.m. to 1 a.m. to 7 a.m. to 7 p.m.; closing some of the dining facilities; and limiting where the board plan (payment system) can be used.

Improving Scheduling

Decreasing or Eliminating Overtime

Overtime should not exceed two percent of the productive hours paid. If overtime is occurring frequently, increasing the full-time staff may be the less expensive solution. The need for overtime is usually a result of poor planning or an accident. If overtime has become a regular needed occurrence, additional flexible-hour employees may be indicated

On the other hand, overtime is being used more and more by some restaurants, and management reasons that a trained, experienced person can produce so much more and maintain quality better than a substitute. It has become a "perk" for employees who may ordinarily work a 30- or 35-hour week to be able to pick up the additional pay when business exceeds the expectation. The costs have to be evaluated by management and if not a weekly occurrence, it may be the best solution to shortages of labor.

Some foodservices have aggressive managers of overtime and may authorize overtime only for work on national holidays, and then require prior management approval for overtime other than holidays.

Using Flexible Schedules and Split Shifts

Allowing employees to work four nine-hour shifts may be to the foodservice operation's advantage and may be preferred by some staff. Such an option should be determined a benefit for the foodservice operation before it is instituted. Management will need to determine if productivity levels stay as high or if the employees are overtired and less productive.

Flexible schedules have a lot a merit, and when employees are cross-trained they can do more than one job. Having employees work in more than one department has proven to reduce costs, providing needed short-hour employees at peak times. Job sharing or job splitting is another effective way to fill positions. For example, two employees can split a 40-hour week between them.

Good planning means having just enough labor when it is needed and never more than is needed. "Leaning time" should be avoided by tracking peaks and valleys of the day and week. Overtime pay indicates either an emergency or improper scheduling.

USING AUTOMATION AND ROBOTICS

Automation and robotics make vending good food a winning way of reducing labor costs in college dorms, hospitals, schools, and B&Is. Vending of food is a convenient way to provide food where and when the customer wants it. Many foods are being provided packaged and ready-to-heat-and-eat . Food being vended no longer means "junk food," but "convenience food." Food can be available 24 hours a day, and labor costs can be kept under control.

HC   Shands Hospital at the University of Florida in Gainesville, a 575-bed facility, has seen vending grow. The big advantage to vending is that it is self-operated and is customer-service-driven. The foodservice director found that stocking the vending machines with their own entrees drove sales up to 6,000 meals a day.

Automated equipment and new technology have been slow to come to the foodservice industry. One exception is the base-heating technology with induction heat. Induction heat is transferred electromagnetically to the food. The surface of the tray or plate remains cool to the touch and can virtually eliminate burns. The induction heat keeps food hot or heats food, resulting in improved efficiency, more efficient use of energy, reduced employee and customer burns from hot plates and trays, and has improved customer satisfaction because food stays hot longer. Induction of heat has great potential in hospitals and restaurants, where food is heated after orders are placed.

HC   The Hillcrest Baptist Medical Center (Waco, TX), using induction heat technology , reports its tray line assembly time has been cut down by 20 minutes per meal time (60 minutes per day). They have had fewer work-related accidents, and the food is better. Even the detergent usage went down because the containers used with heat-induction do not have as many pieces.

Computerizing and Reducing Paperwork

The goal today is to computerize everything and become as paperless as possible. Computerized scheduling of labor is increasing productivity for Marriott. Labor-scheduling software is being used that coordinates traffic (volume of customers) every 15 minutes. The dishwashing staff can be used effectively if cross-trained in service areas and can go in and out of the dishwashing area as needed. Marriott has increased productivity by 8.3% and cut costs in several of its accounts nearly $2 million in two years.

Health cares and university/college foodservices are among the most computerized segments of the industry. They have computerized forecasting, menus and recipes, scheduling of food production, nutritional analyses, attention to food and drug allergies, ordering, and inventory control. The computerized systems often interface with order entry, admissions, discharge, and transfer.

RES Restaurants that have computerized ordering by waitperson have decreased the percentage of food cost because revenue has increased and theft or accommodating a customer with favors to enhance tips has decreased. The waitstaff have realized an increase in sales because their time is more effectively used to wait on customers versus placing orders with the kitchen. In addition, a computerized production record is tracking food items. This assists management with re-ordering, and if the system is totally computerized it drives the re-ordering. The tracking of customer volume by 15-minute intervals can be most valuable when scheduling staff.

SCH ## Cashless System

Some colleges/universities, B&I operations, and school districts have utilized computerized point-of-sale devices to make their programs virtually cashless systems at the point of sale (POS) terminals. A scanable card that can be used by the student to pay for meals in the dining room, copies in the library, and to pay a library fine has merit. Many schools and universities accept credit cards, and debit cards encourage parents to add money to the student's account using the credit cards.

Summary

In summary, management should not consider labor costs a fixed cost that they can do nothing about, but instead should look at innovative ways they can be reduced. Think twice before replacing any employee--question whether the position is needed or if some other arrangement is workable.

5
CONTROLLING FOOD COSTS

CONTENTS

OBJECTIVES OF CHAPTER 5

After studying this chapter, the reader should be able to:

- Understand why the menu is called the driver
- Compare food costs with foodservice industry standards
- Determine how much revenue is available for food
- Determine food costs and how the food dollar is spent
- Identify standard procedures needed
- Precost and postcost recipes and meals
- Identify many ways of reducing food costs
- Determine days and turnover of inventory

Food and beverage cost is one of those prime costs that average between 30%-45% of sales. In the restaurant segment the cost is slightly lower than in most other segments of the foodservice industry. Food costs in hospitals and schools are often on the high end. Controlling food costs becomes more challenging each year as competition becomes greater, numbers of distributors shrink, food prices get higher, customers demand greater value, and foodservices operate on tighter margins. In 1996 food costs had one of the greatest increases in many years; for example, the costs of dairy products and produce took a jump.

To obtain food costs, the following information is needed:

Beginning inventory in dollar value
Plus costs of purchases made during the period
Less the ending inventory in dollar values

Food costs discussed in this chapter include beverage costs, though many commercial restaurants keep them separate, and should do so if the sales are more than 20 percent of the total cost for food and beverages together.

MENU AS THE DRIVER

The menu is the biggest controller, or determinant, of all costs--it is the driver. Planning the right menu mix and knowing when to introduce new items and remove slow ones are secrets to a continual successful menu and foodservice operation. The bottom line is that the menu has to be served within the money available.

Chapter 5 of the text and this chapter of the study guide will not attempt to cover menu planning but will discuss the menu as it affects costs.

Importance of the Menu

The importance of a well-planned menu cannot be overemphasized. For example, Bernstein and Paul in *Winning the Chain Restaurant Game* state that "an excellent menu balance and purchasing efficiencies" can be credited with Olive Garden's steadily rising customer counts and low food costs--30 percent of the revenue.

The importance of the menu--why it is considered the driver--is that it determines every facet of a foodservice operation, as follows:

- Quantity and type food to purchase

- Number of customers who will be served

- Food costs

- Staff skills needed and production schedule

- Facilities and equipment needed

- Nutritional content of food

- Bottom line, or profit

- Customer satisfaction

Fred Turner, former chief executive of McDonald's Corporation, said that in the chain's early days, selling only ten items, having a small facility, and using a limited number of suppliers created an ideal environment for controlling costs.

Menu Mix

The goal for a foodservice operation is to offer menus that have high popularity, low food costs, and a high profit margin--such menus are called winners, or stars. Not all of the menus can fit into this category, and some less popular must be offered. The marginal menu is the one that has high popularity but a low-profit margin. Then there is the menu with low-acceptance but a high-profit-margin menu, and lastly, there is the loser--the one low in acceptance and with a low profit margin, e.g., vegetarian burger. The latter menu should be eliminated from a financial standpoint, but may be kept to appease a group of customers.

It takes a good menu mix to be successful. The Olive Garden restaurant chain has a good menu mix, which is responsible for its popularity and financial success.

Universities and colleges probably offer the most extensive variety of food; e.g., the University of Georgia's dining halls offer more than 300 standard menu items to choose from each day. These items make up a three-week menu cycle. One wonders if this much variety is needed and yet just how far it could be trimmed back before there would be complaints of the cycle's being boring and repetitious, and not having enough variety. Texas A&M University is known for its innovative menu and extensive variety.

STANDARDIZED PROCEDURES

Operating a foodservice should not be a hit or miss situation. Benchmarks can be set and met by using standardized procedures. These include: (1) well-planned menus, which have been precosted, (2) standardized recipes, (3) good purchasing, ordering, and inventory control, and (4) strict portion control. The biggest advantage will be consistency of product and cost--with both the customer and investor being happy with the results.

Use of Standardized Recipes

The number one reason to use standardized recipes is to achieve consistency of product. The second reason is that management can know the food costs.

A standardized recipe lists the ingredients, weights and measures, directions with prescribed times and temperatures, and number and size of servings. If the recipe is followed accurately, the results should be good-- the quality should be consistently good and the customer should be able to depend upon the quality, as well as the size of portions. Occasionally chefs refuse to write out their recipes. However, if a chef is not willing to put his or her specialties into a standardized format, management's risk of not having popular specials after the present chef is gone is too great for management to take.

The first requirement to precosting and postcosting is that a standardized recipe be used. The recipe must be in writing (though it may be memorized), the yield must be known, and the portion size must be controlled.

Value of Precosting Recipes and Meals

Precosting determines if the food item or menu is within the desired cost range. It establishes the ideal costs or potential costs (with little or no waste). If a standardized recipe is precosted, the yield is what it should be, the portion size is correct, and all portions are sold, the precost will have told what the cost is because the precost and postcost will be the same. Seldom does this occur so ideally, because preparing too much or serving larger portions than planned often result in food waste and higher food costs. See Exhibit 5.1, an example of a precosted recipe. Exhibit 5.2 shows an example of a breakdown of food, which makes precosting and postcosting easier to do.

Precosting may be of little value if controls are not carried out during preparation, service, and handling of leftovers.

Determining the Yield

When precosting or postcosting food, it is necessary to determine the yield of the products. For example, the yields of some items vary greatly, as with some meat products, poultry, produce, and fish. Many items have a low yield. The price per pound for the raw product may be low but the product "as served" many be high because of the low yield (loss during preparation is high). For example, the yield of top sirloin beef or leg of lamb may be as low as 59% because of the waste (bones, fat, and trimmings); and 27 pounds of broccoli may yield only 16 pounds of edible product after the tougher parts of the stalk are cut away.

The food cost form in Exhibit 5.3 is used by the Culinary Institute of America and provides the steps that need to be considered when preparing from raw ingredients. The yield of the end product is what is sellable, though the cost includes the cost of all the ingredients.

Exhibit 5.1 Example of a Precosted Recipe

Chili with Beans and Beef		

Size Servings: 8 oz (1 cup)		Number Servings: 110
Preparation Time: 45 minutes		
Total Cost: $ 21.44		Cost Per Serving: $ .195
Cooking Utensil: Kettle, Brazing Pan, or Pot		
Cooking Time: 30 Minutes		Internal Temperature: 170° F

Ingredients	**Quantity**	**Item Cost**
Beef, Ground, 18-20% Fat	5 lb	$ 5.756
Vegetable Protein, Soy	14 oz	0.411
Water	2 ½ cup	-0-
Onions, Dehydrated	1 cup	0.182
Flour, All-Purpose	1 cup	0.042
Water	1 cup	-0-
Kidney Beans, Cooked	4 ½ gal	9.950
Chili Powder, Ground	½ cup + 2 Tbsp	0.499
Tomato Paste	1 gal	4.593
Water	2 qt	-0-
	TOTAL COST	**$21.433**

Instructions
1. Add water to vegetable protein; add water to onions to reconstitute.
2. Brown beef, reconstituted onions, and reconstituted vegetable protein.
3. Make a paste of flour and water; add to meat; stir constantly.
4. Add beans, chili powder, tomato paste, and water to meat mixture.
5. Reduce heat to prevent over-thickening.
6. Transfer to soup crock or pan for service. Add water to thin if needed.

Adapted from: *School Foodservice Management*, 4th ed., by Dorothy Pannell-Martin. Copyright by Van Nostrand Reinhold, 1990, transferred to inTEAM Associates, Inc. 1992.

Exhibit 5.2   Cost Breakdown of Foods to Use in Precosting and Postcosting

Description of Item (1)	Purchase Unit (2)	Cost/ Purchase Unit (3)	Quantity in Purchase Unit (4)	Cost Per Serving or Usable Unit (5)
Meat/Poultry/Seafood:				
Beef, Patties, 4 oz	case	$ 27.76	80	$ .350
Beef, Patties, 2 oz	case	24.19	117	.207
Beef, Steakettes, 6 oz	case	24.00	160	.150
Beef, Stew Meat	lb	34.87	78	.450
Chicken, Breast	case	42.25	40	1.050
Chicken, Tenders	case	22.00	50	.440
Chicken, Patties	case	26.89	90	.299
Vegetables, Frozen/Canned:				
Corn, Niblets	6/10 cans/case	$ 13.45	150 (½ cup)	$ .090
Corn, on Cob, Frozen	case	14.16	96	.150
Beans, Green, Cut	20 lbs	13.68	116	.120
Beans, Kidney	6/10 cans/case	12.13	150 (½ cup)	.096
Potatoes, Dehydrated	6/10 cans	36.81	262 (½ cup)	.140
Potatoes, French Fried	30 lbs	14.82	140 (1 cup)	.110
Potatoes, Hash Browns	30 lbs	17.63	240 (1 cup)	.070

Exhibit 5.3 Food Cost Form

Menu Item_____   Date _____

Number of Portions _____   Size_____

Cost Per Portion _____   Selling Price _____   Cost % _____

INGREDIENTS	RECIPE QUANTITY (EP)			COST			TOTAL COST
	Wgt.	Volume	Count	APS/ Unit	Yield %	EPS/ Unit	
TOTAL RECIPE COST							

Courtesy of the Culinary Institute of America, Hyde Park, NY.

To determine cost per portion:

$$\frac{\text{Total Recipe Cost}}{\text{Number of Portions}} \quad = \quad \underline{\hspace{3cm}} \text{ per Portion}$$

To determine food cost percentage: $\dfrac{\text{Food Cost per Portion}}{\text{Selling Price}} = \underline{\hspace{2cm}}\%$

In many instances, a proportioned, trimmed item that is ready to cook is the best buy. The food preparer should have ways of using most of the trimmings and controlling shrinkage during the cooking process resulting in a better yield than obtained in the ordinary kitchen. This is a different philosophy from that of the "old days," when labor costs were low and most of the trimmings were used.

Reasons for Precosting and Postcosting

Precosting and postcosting are tools for controlling food costs. Precosting **sets standards as to how much a food or menu should cost. Postcosting** checks those standards. Precosting without postcosting is doing half the job. Many managers precost, but few postcost. Generally speaking, it is not the cost of the precosted food that breaks the foodservice operation, but the <u>actual cost</u> of the food at the point of service that causes the deficits.

Often the postcosted meal turns out to be higher than the precosted meal, but it **should not be more than 2 percent higher**. To determine the postcost of a recipe or menu, a record of all foods taken from storage should be made and costed out. The value of leftovers may be deducted if the leftovers will be effectively used later.

To make the job of precosting and postcosting easier, all food and beverage items should be broken down into a useable measurement (Exhibit 5.2). For example, if a 1 ½ pound loaf of white pullman bread costs 78¢ and contains 26 usable slices, each slice is costing 3¢ or $6 for 100 sandwiches. If the bakery delivers a thick-cut loaf of bread with 22 usable slices--each slice is costing 3.6¢ or $7.20 for 100 sandwiches.

As another example, the day's lunch special is a southwest salad with cheese bread and a beverage for $5.95. The precost showed the food cost at 30 percent, or $1.785. However, the postcost showed the cost at 40 percent, or $2.38, because the "chef" added his or her own touches and prepared too many portions ahead of time, sold only 40, and had five left that had to be discarded.

Role of Production Records

The production record provides a form for accumulating the amounts forecasted, prepared, served, and left over, and can be used for postcosting. Exhibit 5.4 provides an example. The real food cost may be easier to check

Exhibit 5.4 Example of a Completed Production Record

InTeam Food System
DAILY FOOD PRODUCTION and POSTCOSTING RECORD

1. DAY OF WEEK: ___TUESDAY-WK 1___   MEAL (BREAKFAST/LUNCH): ___LUNCH___   SCHOOL: _____   DATE: _____

2. NUMBER OF MEALS SERVED (From Cashier Report): _____   STUDENTS: _____   ADULTS/STAFF: _____   TOTAL: _____

3. A LA CARTE SALE OF MENU ITEMS (Number of Portions): _____

4. WEATHER CONDITIONS: _____   5. UNUSUAL CONDITIONS: _____

(6) RECIPE # CODE	(7) MENU MEAL COMPONENT	(8) PORTION SIZES	(9) SERVINGS PER UNIT	(10) PORTIONS PLANNED	(11) QUANTITY FOOD PLANNED	(12) TEMPERATURE BEGIN-NING	ENDING	(13) QUANTITY FOOD PREPARED	(14) LEFTOVERS TO BE USED	(15) QUANTITY USED AND WASTED	(16) NUMBER PORTIONS SERVED	(17a) UNIT COST	(17b) TOTAL COST	(18a) UNIT COST	(18b) TOTAL COST/ VALUE	(19) POSTCOST (17b+18b=19)	(20) COST PER PORTION (19÷16=20)
			FORECAST:100			SERVING INFORMATION						PURCHASED		COMMODITIES		COST FACTOR	
INTM5112B	Spaghetti Sauce/Meat	1 serving	100/rec.	50	1/2 rec.						50	.1004	5.02	.2169	10.845		
INTM301	Taco w/Beef &Cheese	1taco/2.5oz	100/rec.	40	1/2 rec.						40	.2805	11.22	0	0		
INTL013A	Chef Salad "D"	1 serving	100/rec.	10	1/8 rec.						10	.4084	4.084	0	0		
INTV001	Salad, Tossed, no dressing	½ cup	100/rec.	40	1/2 rec.						40	.122	4.88	0	0		
09020	Applesauce, cn, sw, sw/ss	½ cup	6/#10	10	2/3 cn						10	0	0	.056	.56		
19097	Sherbet, orange	1 cup	72/cs	100	3/4 cs.						100	.1562	15.62	0	0		
01082	Milk, lowfat, 1%	½ pint	50/cs	10	10 ea.						10	.1428	1.428	0	0		
01104	Milk, chocolate, lowfat, 1%	½ pint	50/cs	70	1 1/2 cs.						70	.1352	9.464	0	0		
01077	Milk, whole, 3.3% fat	½ pint	50/cs	20	1/2 cs.						20	.1496	2.992	0	0		
INTB020	Bread, French garlic	1 slice	100/rec.	90	1 rec.						90	.079	7.11	0	0		
06164	Salsa, commercial, variety	.25cup	215/cs	40	40 ea.						40	.1055	4.22	0	0		
04021	Salad Dress, Ital, diet	.25 cup	100/cs	20	20 ea.						20	.0314	.628	0	0		
04021	Salad Dress, Ital, diet	2 tbl	100/cs	20	20 ea.						20	.0314	.628	0	0		
04023	Salad dressing 1000 Isl, diet	.25 cup	100/cs	20	20 ea.						20	.032	.64	0	0		
04023	Salad dressing 1000 Isl, diet	2 tbl	100/cs	5	5 ea.						5	.032	.16	0	0		

Total Cost - Portion Cost ____ 1.8064 ____ 68.094 ____ .272 ____ 11.405

Average Meal Cost ____ 0.68094 ____ 0.1140

*Servings per unit may be recipe (rec), pounds (#), cans (cs) and cans (cn)
*Menu portions are for National meeting nutritional requirements of 5 - 11 year old.

_____ Manager or designee

21. COMMENTS:

22. NOTES TO MANAGER. Attach copy of today's menu to production record or the month's menu to the front of the production records for the month and all recipes used.

Exhibit 5.4 Example of a Completed Production Record (continued)

ITEM	INSTRUCTIONS
1.	Complete with day of week, meal, name of foodservice, and date.
2.	Record number of customers
3.	Record dollars in sales.
4.	State weather conditions and/or any unusual events, e.g., flu epidemic, parade in the area, that may have affected the number of customers and sales. This will be important to know the next time the same menu selections are served.
5.	Enter the employee assigned the job.
6.	Put **recipe** number and indicate source. For example, USDA D-20. **If no recipe was used**, leave blank.
7.	List menu items by categories. It may take several pages.
8.	Record the portion sizes; e.g., bread may be 1 roll, meat may be 1 (5 oz.) portion, and mixed vegetables may be 3/4 cup.
9.	State number of servings per purchased unit and the yield.
10.	Forecast number of portions-- how many you think you will serve based on previous times this menu item was served.
11.	Record the quantity of food to be prepared; this refers to pounds, numbers of cans, numbers of dozens, etc.
12.	Record the temperature of food at the beginning of service time. Cold food should be at 45° F or below and, generally speaking, hot food should be at 150° F or higher. Exceptions to this are chicken, at 165° F, and rare beef, at 110° F. Check temperature before service begins and again at end of service to see that equipment is holding food at safe temperatures.
13.	Record actual quantity of food prepared--the amount of food cooked, prepared in pounds, dozens, cans, etc.
14.	Record the usable food leftovers--in bulk quantities or servings.
15.	Subtract the quantities in column 14 from the quantities in column 13. The difference goes in column 15, quantity used and wasted.
16.	Record the number served, which is shown on cashier report (if item is entered at point of sale).
17.	Obtain purchased unit cost from delivery tickets or from the "Product Information" in the inTEAM *Food System for Managers Manual.*
18.	Multiply 17a (cost) by number of units (item 15).
19.	Divide total in column 18 by number of portions served (column 16).
20.	Use this space to make yourself notes for use the next time this menu is served, e.g., waste because a pan was dropped or burned.

Source: *Manager's Production Handbook* by Dorothy Pannell-Martin, Gertrude Applebaum, and Elizabeth Soares. Copyright by inTEAM Associates, Inc., 1998.

as a whole for a day or a meal than individual items. All foods used should be recorded and costed out--with any useable leftovers subtracted. (the leftovers have to be used or they become one of the day's costs). The production record does not have to be a time-consuming chore if everyone in charge of a unit prepares a portion of it.

Having a cycle menu, a cycle of specials of the day, or a repeating menu makes the job easier--then much of the information can be completed before preparation and can be duplicated. The handwritten part can be done on the computer if accessible in the kitchen area. With the cyclical menus the production records from previous days or months become historical data.

Good production records are essential to cost control. The record starts with a forecasted number of portions for each menu item, how much was prepared, and what was left, and it provides a place to postcost food used. The goal is for the forecast and the amount used to be close. Management needs to train employees to record accurately the quantity of food that was used, the number of portions served, and the quantity left over. To avoid listing all ingredients on the production record, the recipe number/source can be referenced (or a copy attached) and the number of portions forecasted and prepared.

Is it a leftover or food waste? A leftover is a food that can be used the next day with slight alteration, whereas food waste is that food that has to be dumped. "Waste forms" are daily records kept at McDonald's and Wendy's.

REVENUE AVAILABLE FOR FOOD

The first step to determining the "ideal food cost" is to identify what the budget is or how much revenue has been earmarked for each meal or the percentage of revenue earmarked for food. Refer to Chapter III,"Establishing Revenue," to see how to determine the revenue available. The revenue available may be called maximum allowable food costs--that amount left after other variable costs and fixed costs have been covered.

Foodservices with set dollar amounts, such as those in health care units and correctional institutions, have budgets of "X" amount per day per person. They need to distribute that money over three or more meals a day. For example, a hospital foodservice's revenue generally comes from providing services to patients and nonpatients. Though the patient portion of the revenue is a budgeted amount, the nonpatient portion is usually in the form of cash that is collected at the point-of-sale or service or is billed to another department for staff meals.

A restaurant owner may establish a menu and the cost, then the price to be charged. But regardless of which way one arrives at the revenue, it is important to have a standard set for food costs--influenced by peers in the foodservice industry, by the customers, by personal goals, etc. The portion of the budget designated for food is generally between 30 and 45 percent of the revenue (30% for restaurants and 35%-45% for other segments). A private club may run a food cost as high as 50% because upper management wants top-quality food and low prices.

Determining Percentage of Revenue Used for Food

To determine what percentage of the revenue that is actually used for food, one must determine the food costs. This is done by taking **the beginning inventory and adding the costs of foods and beverages purchased, then subtracting from the total value of the ending inventory**. See Exhibit 5.5 for steps to determining food and beverage costs. If an accurate perpetual inventory is not maintained, a physical inventory should be taken weekly or, at a minimum, monthly.

Exhibit 5.5   Sample of Determining Food and Beverage Costs

To Figure Food Cost for a Week: Beginning-of-Week Food Inventory[1] + Food Purchases During Week – End-of-Week Inventory	$ 4,782 + 16,862 – 4,375
Total Weekly Cost of Food Used	$ 16,269/Week
Divide by the Number of Days of Business to Determine the Daily Food Cost (e.g., $16, 269 ÷ 6 business days =)	$ 2,712/Day

To determine the percentage of revenue spent for food in Exhibit 5.5, divide the food costs by the revenue/sales, as shown below:

Food Costs ($2,712)   ÷   Revenue/Sales ($7,200)   =   37.7% Food Costs

[1]Note: The end-of-month inventory is next month's beginning inventory.

Standards in Different Segments of the Industry

The different segments of the foodservice industry have different goals, and the profit margin desired varies greatly. As a result, the percentage of the revenue spent for food ranges from the low 20s to low 50s. This is expected to change in the next five years because of the focus on profits, and many of those with high food costs are having to be self-supporting.

RES   The restaurant segment of the foodservice industry usually runs one of the lower food costs, between 30 and 35 percent of the revenue. Outback Steak Houses run one of the higher food costs--39 percent--but providing top-quality food is one of their selling points. That is approximately 6 percent more than the average food cost of 33 percent among most mid-scale restaurants. Olive Garden has one of the lowest food costs with 30 percent, which management contributes to efficient purchasing and an excellent menu balance (mix). Taco Bell restaurants have one of the most controlled food costs at 32%.

U&C
COR   Universities/colleges and correctional institutions have a wide range of food costs--between 26 and 50 percent of the revenue. This can be attributed (in part) to the "uncontrolled portions" philosophy of "as much as the student wants." See Exhibit 5.6.

HC   Health care units, especially extended care units, have high food costs because of the prescribed special diets and supplements, and the plate waste is extremely high.

B&I
SCH   The food costs for self-operated B&Is and schools are usually in the 40 to 50 percent range because of the low markup above costs with prices charged generally under the going rates on the outside. For example, schools will have revenue around $2 for a lunch meal, meaning there may be only 76¢-80¢ to spend for food. With the nutritional guidelines that specify ½ pint of milk and no more than 30 percent of the calories from fat, the costs of each menu component run higher than one might expect.

Exhibit 5.6 Sample of Food/Beverage and Labor Costs at Some Leading Universities and Colleges

University/College	Percentage of Revenue Spent for Food	Percentage of Revenue Spent for Labor
Michigan State University	32.5	27.7
Penn State University	36.0	35.9
Harvard University	26.7	46.0
Brigham Young University	52.0	29.8
Rutgers University	26.4	36.9
Purdue University	26.2	32.6
University of Maryland	31.9	36.6
Miami University	29.0	45.6

Exhibit 5.6 illustrates the range in food/beverage costs at some leading universities and colleges. For example, 35 contract-run facilities reported in a survey that their food costs in the university/college segment rose from 39% to 41.5% over a period of two years. The survey of the food costs (in Exhibit 5.6) shows that food costs are running between 26% and 52% in the universities. One may quickly say the 52% is too high--however, it depends on the goals of the people in charge.

How the Food Dollar Is Spent

If food costs are running high, the manager should break down the costs and determine for what the food dollar is spent. Most distributors can provide the manager with a breakout by category of food with dollars spent. If the manager has more than one unit, comparing units and the food breakout by category can be revealing. The questions are, "what percentages of the food dollar are being spent for entrees, dairy products, produce, alcoholic beverages, outside bakery-made items, frozen foods, staples, etc.?" Compare these breakouts from one period to another--and from one item to another.

Some managers use the "ABC formula" (described below) of watching those foods that cost the most and taking a physical inventory frequently or keeping a perpetual inventory on the items designated as "A" foods. Using the ABC formula, food products are divided into the following categories:

A = Foods that are highest in costs, e.g., maybe 15%-20% in volume or quantity, but may account for 75% of the total dollars, such as meats, poultry, and fish

B = Foods that are of medium cost, such as cheese and frozen foods

C = Foods that are low in value but may occupy half of the storeroom, such as catsup, sugar, flour, and shortening

The "A" foods with the highest value are tracked more carefully than the foods that are classified as "C." Tracking food and supplies from the back door (delivery) to the front door (service) is possible and easier today than ever before through a good production record and computerized point of sale. An example of how the food dollar may be used is shown in Exhibit 5.7.

Employee Meals

Some argue that food costs should be calculated only on food served to paying customers, not employees. Meals eaten by staff are still food costs, and one could argue that they should be included in the food costs because they should not be a large proportion of the food dollar. If the employee meals amount to large numbers, the meals should be identified separately. The restaurant segment is more likely to separate the costs of employee meals out of the total food costs. If employee meals are to be removed from the food costs, the average costs can be arrived at as follows:

Average Costs of a Meal x Number of Employees = Employee Food Costs

Exhibit 5.7 Example of How the Food Dollar Is Spent

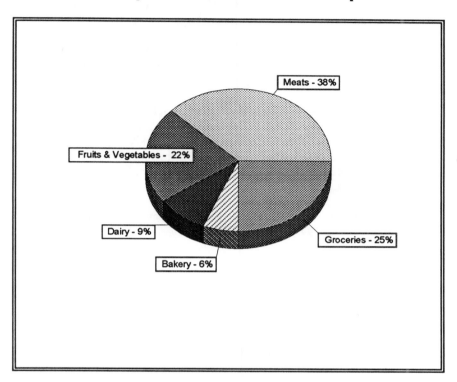

Another issue to be dealt with is, "should employees be charged for their food?" Many operations do charge employees for meals, but the question to answer is, "what does it accomplish?" Do employees nibble while preparing or serving food, or snitch food while no one is looking, or do they bring food from home to put in the refrigerator? Management policy needs to be established--whether the meal is free or is discounted or at full prices. What does the meal consist of? Are there any limitations? Such limitations should be established in operational policy and enforced.

It is important to capture the number of employee meals consumed for a real food cost for the food sales. Additionally, restaurants should capture the employee meals because of the Fair Labor Standards Act (1967), which requires that the waitstaff be paid the federal minimum wage. The employer can reduce the minimum wage by the value of the meal prorated over hours worked. For example,

If the minimum wage is $5.40 and the meal is charged at the reasonable cost of $2.50, divide $2.50 by number of hours worked (8)   (= $ .320)

$ 5.40 Minimum Wage
-    .32 Food Allowance
$ 5.08 Wage Rate

REDUCING FOOD COSTS

When food costs are too high, management needs to determine why, and solve the problem. Is the sale price too low, or is the food on the menu too expensive? Is there a good menu mix? Is there too much waste? Other factors may cause high food costs, such as theft and some federal regulations.

For example, the Religious Freedom Restoration Act of 1993 has forced some institutional foodservices to comply with diets prescribed by the religious doctrine ,and in doing so, has increased food costs. An example is the penal institutions that must comply with diets prescribed by the inmates' religions. One penal institution reported an average food cost of $2.74 a day for the regular inmate and $4.50 a day for an inmate served a diet prescribed for religious reasons. This regulation can tax an already limited budget.

The schools that are participating in the National School Lunch and Child Nutrition Program are being faced with meeting dietary guidelines that will increase food costs. Some regulations, such as these two mentioned, may increase food costs; however, food costs can be lowered in other ways, such as those described below.

Most operations can reduce food costs by three to four percent and not negatively affect quality. The food cost reductions can be made by reducing food waste. The executive chef who is cost-conscious will train cooks in how to reduce food waste; e.g., use stems of asparagus and broccoli to make excellent asparagus or broccoli soup. However, if labor costs are high it may not be a savings to spend the labor hours necessary to utilize all parts, and it may be more cost effective to purchase already trimmed asparagus and broccoli. Many school districts have rejected some USDA commodities because the food was more expensive to prepare than they saved by using the "free food."

There are many ways to reduce costs--start with well-planned menus and lower prices paid for the ingredients, and good portion control with the food.

Re-Engineering the Menu

Re-engineering the menu may mean reducing choices and the lengths of the menu cycles. From evaluating participation or sales by menu item, most managers learn that 8-10 items provide 70 percent of the sales. Some of the ways different foodservices have reduced costs are as follows:

HC
- With patient stays shorter today, many hospitals have moved from a 12-day or 21-day menu cycle to a 7-day cycle to reduce food costs.

- Some hospitals believe in the three-meal plan with three nourishment offerings. Others have gone to a five-meal plan, which consists of an early continental breakfast, a midmorning brunch, a light early-afternoon refreshment, a late-afternoon main meal, and an evening snack. For some hospitals this reduces the number of employees needed in the early morning and in the late evening. Patient satisfaction and acceptance with the 5-meal plan has not been uniform throughout the country. Traditions and expectations become factors.

U&C
SCH
- Many are reducing costs by moving from a monthly menu cycle to a five-day or ten-day cycle in schools, 14-day for universities/colleges.

- Selling brand foods (e.g., Pizza Hut pizza, Subway sandwiches) has become very popular in many segments of the industry resulting in increased food costs (because the food costs contain labor). These increases in food costs need to be offset by a lowered labor cost; otherwise, generating more sales may not mean more profits.

- Identifying the exact cost of each item on the menu, as well as condiments.

- Checking plate waste to determine if portions are too large.

- Questioning if every item on the plate is needed. Many hospitals have reduced not only food costs, but labor costs as well, by eliminating menu items.

Reducing the Prices Paid for Food

Reducing the prices paid for food is becoming more and more important. There is more being done in this particular area to reduce costs than in all the other areas, as can be seen with the following examples:

- Paying bills on time and taking advantage of discounts.

- Avoiding emergency purchasing at the corner grocery store by improving forecasting and ordering procedures.

RES
- Shopping at warehouse clubs. For small restaurants this may be cost-effective because foods and supplies are sold by the case and in bulk packaging. (The time used to shop should be a part of the cost when comparing costs.)

- Buying on competitive bids--either formal bid or informal bid . The informal process may be as simple as buying on competitive bids-- obtaining price quotes from several companies weekly via fax machine. See example in Exhibit 5.8. Each company should be provided specifications for each of the products. The formal bid process is more structured and requires that written prices be submitted and held for a period of time.

- Using "one-stop shopping" by reducing the number of deliveries made or using a "prime vendor." There are many vendors that can serve as "prime vendors" because they have "full houses"--that is, they furnish most or all of the foods needed. By reducing the number of deliveries, and thereby the number of vendors, a vendor does not have to make as many trips to a location and the orders are larger, reducing their costs and the price paid.

- Using contract purchasing. This involves a signed formal contract and usually results in good prices, whereas the non-contract (informal agreement) is more of a "gentleman's agreement." The safest contract and usually the best prices are obtained with a bid contract because by law the contract must be adhered to.

- Using a prime vendor. This is a little different from one-stop shopping. The prime vendor agreement between a foodservice operator or the vendor is more formal, and usually from 60 to 80 percent of the foods are purchased from the prime vendor. The foodservice operation needs specifications and estimated volume used over a specific period of time and have the option to extend the prices over the following year.

- Using cost-plus purchasing. This means the distributor charges the purchaser cost plus a specific dollar amount (or percentage). If the cost-plus purchasing arrangement is allowed, the foodservice representative will need to keep the vendor honest by requesting proof of prices going up.

Another effective method of cost-plus purchasing is the price of the commodity, such as coffee, beef, poultry, pork, or cheese. The prices of the commodity are published in the financial newspapers, including the *Wall Street Journal*. The prices vary weekly, but the distributor's price is quoted on a fixed percentage (not allowed in some government-controlled foodservice segments) or as dollars to be added to the commodity price. Most independent single-unit owners/managers cannot take advantage of cost-plus purchasing, but certainly large chains, group cooperative members, and large school districts can take advantage of it.

Shopping for the best price using the computerized database from major distributors can result in minor changes in specifications and yielding substantial savings. The four major (or largest) distributors in volume are Kraft, Sysco, Alliant, and Rykoff-Sexton, and all four have regional warehouses.

Exhibit 5.8 Produce Quotes

Item/Pack (1)	Quantity (2)	McKeen's Produce		Smithville Produce		Gordon Foods	
		Each (3)	Total (4)	Each (5)	Total (6)	Each (7)	Total (8)
Apples, 125 count red delicious	4 cs.	$ 17.33	$ 69.32	$19.50	$78.00	$14.50	$58.00
Bananas, 150 petite	2 cs.	21.50	43.00	16.50	33.00	14.00	28.00
Broccoli, stalk	3 ea.	1.40	4.20	1.55	4.65	.90	2.70
Cabbage, lb. red	10 lb.	.80	8.00	.82	8.20	.30	3.00
Cabbage, 50 lb. green/white	5 bag	12.50	62.50	11.50	57.50	12.50	62.50
Carrots, lb. cello pack	5 lb.	.35	1.75	.40	2.00	.25	1.25
Carrots, 50 lb.	1 bag	12.30	12.30	11.90	11.90	12.40	12.40
Cauliflower, head	10 ea.	1.50	15.00	1.49	14.90	1.25	12.50
Grapes, lb. red, seedless	20 lb.	1.35	27.00	1.36	27.20	1.25	25.00
Grapes, lb. white, seedless	20 lb.	2.10	42.00	1.29	25.80	1.35	27.00
Kale, lb.	6 lb.	1.00	6.00	1.10	6.60	.95	5.70
Lettuce, 24 head	6 cs.	19.50	117.00	14.75	88.50	7.75	46.50
Lettuce, leaf head	10 heads	.80	8.00	.75	7.50	.82	8.20
Radishes, lb. cello bag	15 bags	.55	8.25	.25	3.75	.40	6.00
Romaine, head	12 heads	.90	10.80	.40	4.80	.62	7.44
Spinach, 10 oz. cello bag	10 bags	1.00	10.00	1.00	10.00	1.15	11.50
TOTALS		$ 94.88	$ 445.12	$84.56	$ 384.30	$70.39	$317.69

Some large companies have their own distribution centers and can obtain excellent truckload prices. For example, Marriott Distribution Services has 13 distribution centers and is opening five more in 1998-99. It carries a limited-line inventory and has international buying power. Marriott sells to its own accounts and to others. As many as 65% of their customers are from outside the Marriott accounts, and 35% are internal.

- Examining how the food dollar is being used. This can help pinpoint problem areas. This breakdown on what was purchased by location/delivery site can be provided by many of the major distributors.

- Purchasing as a part of a group or a purchasing cooperative. This has become very popular among schools, health care organizations, and correctional institutions. The foodservices' cost savings can be as much as 20 percent. There are other advantages to having "buying power" or "clout" with a group, such as product standardization, improved quality, decreased administrative time, and better service. In the group-purchasing agreements, the purchaser should negotiate for any price allowances or rebates that distributors receive from the manufacturers.

- Reducing errors in orders placed with kitchen. The waitstaff can reduce errors in orders and reduce take-backs by repeating orders placed with choices made by guest.

- Reducing the amount of waste. The waste can be determined by checking what customers eat and what has to be discarded (but untouched). For example, the waste of bread can be reduced by allowing 1 ½ pieces of bread per guest and 1 ½ pats of butter per person--a party of four served 6 rolls and 6 pats of butter.

- Avoiding waste of condiments. For example, coffee drinkers can be asked if they want cream.

- Checking incoming shipments. Someone should check to see that the items invoiced are received and that the condition of products received is acceptable.

HC   Some examples of how cooperative purchasing groups have reduced costs are listed below: A group hospital purchasing unit in Texas called "Opportunity" has 1400 members and is purchasing for the entire facility (not just foodservices). Their contract with vendors provides an additional

7 percent savings if 95 percent of their purchases are from the contractor. They have realized $850,000 savings in three years.

As of January 1, 1998, the Voluntary Hospital Association (VHA) has merged with the University Hospital Consortium (Chicago), a membership of 70 major academic hospitals, and has formed a new corporation called Novation, which is now the largest hospital purchasing group in the United States.

Premier, based in San Diego, is another national health care purchasing group with 1800 members. Their agreement with distributors means about $1 billion in volume for the distributor, which may result in the distributor reducing the margin of profit on each item.

SCH   In South Carolina and Texas the United States Department of Agriculture is piloting purchasing locally commodity foods for the schools. The states expect the economy of a statewide bid to yield a 5 to 10 percent savings. Mississippi and Montana have found that statewide cooperative purchasing for the schools has reduced their food costs.

- Purchasing in bulk for large commissaries and kitchens can result in savings. Any time a half to a whole truckload can be purchased at a time and delivered to one location (warehouse), savings will be realized. However, one should question the cost effectiveness of an organization warehousing and distributing its food. Some of the most successful chain restaurants, e.g. McDonald's, have chosen to stay out of manufacturing of food in commissaries, warehousing, and distributing, and let those who are specialist do those jobs.

- Using the appropriate quality ingredients in recipes can mean lower grades and lower prices. For example, a peach cobbler does not require a beautiful Grade A peach half. The maraschino cherry on the top of cottage cheese or fruit salad does not need a stem in it, and, depending on the price range of the foodservice, it may not need to be a whole maraschino cherry--cherry pieces may do the job of garnishing. And, if a worker is slicing olives for the salad bar, it may be more cost-effective to purchase olive pieces.

- Having soy concentrate and soy isolates added to beef, pork, and poultry is a way of reducing ingredient costs, decreasing fat, increasing yields, and increasing moisture retention in the products.

Using lean ground beef combined with rehydrated soy protein up to a 70:30 ratio in highly seasoned dishes is particularly cost-effective and improves some products, e.g., taco filling, spaghetti meat sauce. For a foodservice operation that uses 5,000 pounds of ground beef a week, a 70:30 ratio (replacing 30% of the lean ground beef with hydrated soy protein) will save approximately $40,000 a year in food costs. Soy protein costs an average of 75¢ per pound as compared to 100% beef at 98¢ per pound. If one pound of ground beef can be extended to make 1.3 pounds then the total cost per portion is less.

Texas A&M under Fred Dollar's leadership used to run taste panels to determine how much soy protein, if any, should be mixed with ground beef used in making hamburgers. A mixture with 10% wet weight soy protein scored higher than any other combination, including 100% beef.

- Comparing prices of well-known brands with those less well-known, and comparing domestic packed foods with the imported packed products may result in a savings. It is worth shopping for the best product for the job at the best price.

HC - Many hospital foodservices have joined hospital cooperatives, resulting in considerable savings. Having to be flexible and purchasing every possible product through bid contracts has resulted in reduced food costs.

The Paradise Valley Hospital (National City, CA) has reduced scratch-prepared items after reviewing production labor, waste, and shelf life of scratch-prepared items with prepared and individually packaged items, such as custards, puddings, cut-up fresh fruit, and gelatin. The hospital management also has accessed the distributor's order-entry software to search the inventory and has identified the lowest-cost items in various product categories and has made substitutions when possible to the lower cost items.

COR - The Milwaukee County (WI) House of Corrections takes advantage of "opportunity purchasing"--buying orders rejected by restaurants and other foodservice facilities. Being flexible and being able to purchase off bid saves money in such cases.

Improving Forecasting and Ordering

Forecasting and ordering are as difficult a task for fast-food restaurants with a limited, repeating menu, or for a restaurant with limited "specials of the day," as they are for foodservice operations with four- to six-week menu cycles or menus that change constantly.

Forecasting the proper quantity of food needed should not be an "off the top of the head" guess for any foodservice operation, but a planned estimate of usage based on facts. Managers of foodservice operations with changing menus often have difficulty with forecasting how many portions to prepare of each menu item. If there are several food items on the menu and the foodservice expects to serve "X" customers today, there are four steps to forecasting accurately, as follows:

1. Plan cyclical menus.

2. Forecast number of portions (the amount) of each menu item needed for a particular period of time.

3. Use sales history and production records.

4. Evaluate the season, events, etc., that may influence sales.

5. Refer back to the recipes and lists of ingredients needed.

How much to order is one of the hardest things for a new manager or purchasing agent to learn. Many of the chain restaurants have solved this problem with the point-of-sale devices that provide ordering information. The steps are best shown by the flowchart in Exhibit 5.9.

Exhibit 5.9   Flowcharts of Forecasting and Ordering Process

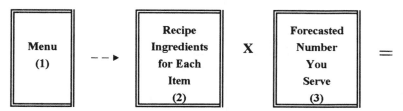

| Menu (1) | $--\blacktriangleright$ | Recipe Ingredients for Each Item (2) | X | Forecasted Number You Serve (3) | = |

| Items and Quantity Needed for Time Period (4) |

| Items and Quantity Needed (4) | + (Plus) | Quantity to Be Used Until Order Received (5) | = | Total Quantity Needed (6) | — (Minus) |

| Quantity in Inventory (7) | = | Amount to Order (8) | $--\blacktriangleright$ | Conversion to Purchase Units (9) |

Exhibit 5.9   Flowcharts of Forecasting and Ordering Process (continued)

STEPS TO FORECASTING
Following are the steps for a manager to follow in ordering:

STEP 1:   Plan ahead, begin preparing order with ample time before it is due.

STEP 2:   Start with the menu for period of time you are ordering. Pull recipes for all the menu items, whereby you order all ingredients needed to prepare the recipes.

STEP 3:   Forecast how many of each portion you will serve. When more than one choice are provided, the percentage of each choice must be figured <u>or</u> the previous production records must be used, which provide the history of how many were served the last time this menu was served. Multiply number. Extend out quantity of ingredients needed.

   If you are computerized, put the forecasted numbers into the computer. If your perpetual inventory is correct, your order will be correctly prepared for you.

   If you are not computerized, ADD the number of portions needed together for each item; take a physical inventory or use the perpetual inventory if up to date. Subtract from inventory forecasted food usage up until delivery arrives (including use for previously placed orders).

STEP 4:   Extend out quantity of ingredients/foods needed to prepare the number forecasted. Convert the number of portions needed to purchase units, always rounding up the quantities. Transfer figures to order form.

STEP 5:   Use a copy of your order to check in deliveries, so that shortages can be spotted immediately and corrective action taken.

Source: inTEAM *Food System Administrator's Manual* **by Dorothy Pannell-Martin and Gertrude Applebaum.   Copyright by inTEAM Associates, Inc. 1995.**

The forecasting and preparing of quantities of food to order has been computerized and is used by many foodservices, and the results are much more accurate forecasting of needs and substantially reduced food costs. There are many point-of-sale systems that are dictating the forecasted numbers--a hamburger ordered by the customer results in a bun, a pattie, and catsup ordered from the vendors. Waste has to be justified/acknowledged daily to avoid shortages in food orders for the next time served.

- Use production boards and records to improve forecasting. A production board is a six-foot-wide white board on which you write with felt tip pens. The main menu items are listed with quantities used; each day the quantities are adjusted as changes occur.

- Computerize the records and nutrient analyses done in the hospital dietitian's office.

- Computerize ordering with an on-line ordering system, which gives faster turn-around than manually placing orders. The closer to delivery an order can be placed, the better is forecasting, and the lower the inventory and loss due to spoilage.

- Purchase precut salad greens if it is more cost-effective than purchasing heads of salad greens and cutting them for salad. A Mexican restaurant or a sub shop that uses a lot of shredded lettuce realizes a cost savings from purchasing the lettuce pre-shredded.

HC
- Reduce the number of unused trays delivered and food not consumed by checking patient admissions and discharges just before each meal.

Maintaining a Par Stock Level

Using a par stock level system means maintaining an optimal level of some items in inventory. The minimum, maximum, and optimal inventory quantities are set for high-use items and staples. That minimum quantity is maintained in stock at all times and a maximum level is not exceeded. The par stock level system works best for foodservice operations with daily or weekly repeating menus/food offerings or twelve months of the year operations, and where there is a reliable delivery system.

The maximum inventory levels should be set carefully, whereby the amount of money tied up in inventory is kept low. For example, french fries and catsup are essential for many foodservice operations--management does not ever want to run out, but on the other hand, an "endless" supply ties up not only money but storage space, and if not rotated on a regular basis can become food waste/spoilage.

The reorder point has to be set considering a lot of factors. Establishing the "reorder" point is a challenge for management unless good records have been maintained on usage. Par stock levels--minimum, maximum, and optimal quantities and the reorder point--should be established considering the following:

- Quantity used
- Frequency of deliveries
- Unit of purchase
- Quantity pricing by the vendor
- Shelf life of product
- Cash flow
- Differences in seasonal usage

The advantages to establishing a par stock level are that the forecasting/ordering processes become much simpler and accurate. Once the reorder point has been reached, the quantity to be ordered is the difference between the reorder point and maximum quantity plus the quantity that will be used between the ordering and delivery.

Maximum Stock Level – Reorder Point = Amount Needed at Time

Amount Needed + Usage before Delivery = Amount to Order

This process is easy to computerize and requires little decision-making once the levels of stock have been established.

The disadvantages are that poorly set par levels can be disastrous--if too low or too high. Some of the problems that can occur when par stock levels are depended upon too heavily are:

- Shortages or overstocking because of peaks and valleys of usage--seasonal needs not considered

- Deliveries not possible because of weather conditions certain times of the year

- Spoilage because of storage facilities' temperatures certain times of the year

- Potential of theft possibly greater

- Too much money possibly tied up in inventory

- Items falling out of favor not being used up

- Items in the par stock system that should not be in; e.g., specials, seasonal items

- Foodservice operations that are closed for periods having unneeded inventory

It is always wise to consider needs and potential changes in needs at the time when ordering.

Improving Receiving Procedures

With good receiving practices, management can reduce or eliminate distributor theft at the point of receiving. The person responsible for receiving needs training in how to properly receive food and what to check. The tools needed are:

- Orders to be delivered with quantities and brief descriptions
- Specifications of products with prices agreed upon
- Scales for weighing products sold by the pound
- Calculator
- Pad of credit memos (see Exhibit 5.10)

Someone responsible and trained should check in deliveries carefully; check produce for quality; count piece items; and weigh items purchase by weight. If prices were previously agreed upon, staff should check to ensure they are the prices charged. If the delivery ticket prices have been manually extended out, staff should check multiplication.

When shortages occur, credit slips should be prepared while delivery person is there. By preparing a credit slip when shortages occur or when rejecting products, the driver is made aware of the problem. The credit slip should be prepared in triplicate and the signatures of the driver and the one preparing the credit slip should be obtained. One copy is for the driver to take back to his or her company, one for the accounting office, and one for the on-site manager. Many people merely note the shortage on the delivery document, and that is acceptable if all parties are picking up the shortages.

Exhibit 5.10   Sample Request for Credit

Number _____

GENERAL HOSPITAL

REQUEST FOR CREDIT

Company_____   From_____

_____

Credit is requested on the items listed below. Invoice #_____   Date_____

Product	Unit of Order	Quantity	Price Per Unit	Total Price

Comments_____

_____

_____

_____   _____

Delivery Person

White Copy, Vendor; Yellow Copy, Accounts Payable; Pink Copy, Foodservice Manager

Improving Inventory Control

Inventory should be controlled as tightly as cash. Inventory is considered an asset under an accrual accounting system; however, inventory should be kept low because it is tying up money that could be drawing interest. The first step to good inventory control is a system of counting inventory. The two systems of counting inventory are perpetual and physical. With a perpetual inventory a physical inventory is still necessary, but a physical inventory can be kept without a perpetual. The questions often asked are (1) can a perpetual inventory be justified? and (2) how often should physical inventory be taken if there is no perpetual inventory?

One of the best methods of inventorying a large warehouse is to physically count only one (randomly selected) category of items in a set time frame. Within a period of one month, three months, or six months, inventory all items in the warehouse. Automated data processing has not replaced the need for an accurate physical inventory.

Perpetual Inventory

A perpetual inventory is a running record of the quantities of products on hand. This record is accomplished by recording each product as received and added to stock and amounts removed from stock. At any given time the balance on hand should be the amount in inventory. Maintaining a perpetual inventory is time-consuming, and it is difficult to maintain with accuracy even with a computer. If a requisition system is used, if the foodservice produces for large numbers, or if the foodservice is a central production kitchen, then a perpetual inventory should be required. It is an excellent cost-control measure.

Perpetual inventories are checked for accuracy with a daily physical inventory (or change in employees--shift change). This can certainly be justified for the high-priced items, especially alcoholic beverages. It is not necessary to even enter the data into the computer, unless a hand-held input device is being used when physically counting the items. Instead, the record of inventory becomes a part of the checkout each day. Checks and balances are necessary to detect theft or prevent it; thus different people (usually management) may need to do the physical checkout once a month at unexpected times.

The accuracy of the perpetual inventory should be checked at least monthly by taking a physical inventory of all items. If the accuracy of the perpetual inventory is good, then the physical inventory could be of some items each month (different items) and the dollar value of inventory at the end of the month used as the ending inventory.

Physical Inventory

A physical inventory is a manual counting of items in stock. If a perpetual inventory is not being kept, a physical inventory should be taken prior to placing orders. Fast-food restaurants may require that a physical inventory be completed before a shift of employees changes. Aramark, a leading foodservice management company, requires a weekly physical inventory and limits the quantity in stock to no more than seven days of inventory at any one time. In some health care facilities, a maximum of three days of inventory is maintained. The use of prime vendors has substantially reduced how much money has to be invested in inventory.

The accuracy of the dollar value of the inventory and when the inventory is taken are important to the accuracy of the food costs on the profit and loss statement. The inventory should be taken at the end of the month (or when the accounting system time period designates--for example, from the 15th of one month to the 15th of the next) and the end of the day. It should be taken at a minimum monthly, before an operating statement or profit and loss statement is prepared. The value of the inventory will differ based on the prices used when determining the value of the inventory.

Evaluating the inventory--there are several means of evaluating inventory: (1) actual price paid, (2) weighted price if product was purchased at different prices, (3) lowest price paid (based on FIFO--"first in first out" practice) or (4) highest price paid (based on LIFO--"last in first out"-- practice [not a recommended practice, although this is generally used when reporting to Internal Revenue Service and if management wants to inflate the value of the inventory]). Using the same means of evaluating the inventory each time is important because the impact on profits can be great.

Two people should take the physical inventory--with one recording and the other calling out items and counting what is in stock. Some Japanese companies have proven that "just-in-time" purchasing can work for them if there is cooperation of the vendors--and it can work for most foodservice operations. However, some of the foodservice operations in remote areas and in small-volume foodservices may not be able to obtain deliveries frequently and may have to carry larger inventories.

Many believe that high inventories foster high food costs; thus their goal is to keep the inventory as low as possible. Others recommend large-quantity purchases, supplies that will last several months. The larger inventories may be feasible for non-commercial foodservices, but the trend is toward keeping inventory low. How large the foodservice is will make a difference. Purchasing of small quantities can be very costly because of the delivery costs.

Days and Turnover of Inventory

One of the best ways of determining if the inventory is too high is to determine how many days of inventory are in stock or how many turnovers in inventory are occurring each month. Ideally there would not be any more in inventory at any one time than is needed before the next delivery. If there are weekly deliveries, no more than seven days of inventory (or four turnovers a month) are needed. To determine how many days of inventory are in stock, one must determine the average daily food costs and divide the dollar value of the ending inventory by the average daily food costs.

To determine the number of days in inventory, it is necessary to calculate the average daily food costs and divide the ending inventory by the daily food costs. See Exhibit 5.11 for an example.

To determine the number of inventory turnovers, it is necessary to divide the average number of days in a month open for business by the number of days in inventory. See Exhibit 5.11 for an example and instructions for determining the number of days of inventory and the number of turnovers.

Exhibit 5.11   Number of Days in Inventory and Inventory Turnovers

Beginning of the month inventory	$ 7,590
+ Food purchased during month	28,509
- Ending of the month inventory	8,450
= Food cost for month	$27,649
Food cost for month	$27,649
÷ Number of days opened in month	÷ 26
= Average daily food cost	= $1,063
Ending of month inventory	$8,450
÷ Average daily food cost	÷ $1,063
= Average number of days in inventory	= 7.9
Average number of days open in month	26
÷ Average number of days in inventory	÷ 7.9
= Average number of turnovers	= 3.3

Improving Inventory Practices

There are many ways to improve inventory practices, such as reducing the quantity in stock. The saying goes, "show me a large inventory and I'll show you high food cost," because it is natural to use more if there is a lot. "The more we have the more we use." Some examples of ways to improve inventory practices are as follows:

- Keep "parstock" adjusted to needs. Parstock, which is the amount of stock needed on the shelves between deliveries, may **not** be advisable for foodservice operations that change menus frequently or that are closed part of the year, e.g., dining hall in a college dorm that is closed for the summer. Over-stocking can be a problem that a good manager or chef should be able to control.

- Reduce number of items in inventory. For example, reduce the spice selection by using mixes when feasible, e.g. spaghetti sauce mix. Spices have a short shelf life and can tie up a lot of money.

- Make several menu selections from one meat, e.g., fillet of chicken breast with three to four different sauces, strips on chef salad, in pasta dish, and in a sandwich.

- Keep low inventory with no more than a seven-day supply.

- Maintain perpetual inventory on key items (expensive items, e.g., lobster).

- At minimum take physical inventory of key items weekly before orders are placed.

- Keep storeroom and large freezer locked except when supplies for the day are being transferred to work areas.

- Store foods at proper temperatures and rotate inventory. Avoid waste by using food before it has spoiled.

- Record temperatures of storage areas daily and instruct on procedures when refrigeration is above the ideal temperatures.

- Evaluate the need to continue purchasing items that move slowly.

- Evaluate the number of spices in inventory and determine what can be eliminated.

HC - Centralize storage and avoid having supplies stored in many areas. Eliminate nourishment centers (where food is maintained) on each patient floor because there is often high usage by unauthorized people and thus a high-waste factor.

Improving Preparation Procedures

Most kitchens can afford to improve preparation procedures and in turn reduce waste and costs. It is often revealing when the amount of food prepared is compared to the food sold. Identifying where food goes is good management. Charge out food to the lounge, to other services, to coffee shops, etc. Several examples and suggestions for improving preparation procedures and reducing costs are as follows:

- Centralize preparation as much as feasible for better food cost controls and lowering of labor costs.

- Adjust recipes to the number of servings needed. For example, if on Monday you will sell 75 portions of spaghetti and meat sauce, Tuesday 75, Wednesday 100, Thursday 90, Friday 225, Saturday 200, the recipe needs to be adjusted and prepared accordingly or the meat sauce needs to be prepared twice a week for three days based on good forecasted figures.

  Check out all the seasonings and prepared sauces--do some blind testing of products cooked different lengths of time. If cooking time for a product can be reduced, it may be more cost-effective to prepare daily what you expect to use. Have the recipes adjusted accordingly. If the recipe is on computer, it will be easy to adjust the recipe to accommodate the different quantities needed.

- Batch-cook for improved quality and fewer leftovers. Pre-prepare food for batch cooking, which speeds up preparation time when the product is needed. Restaurants may find *"sous vide"* advisable (cook/chill individual or batches of entrees ready for finishing off).

- Check recipe yield and determine if the recipe is yielding the projected number of portions. For example, meat sauce simmering on the back of the stove for long periods of time will often have reduced quantity as well as quality.

- Establish an "ingredient room" procedure whereby ingredients are weighed and measured by one or two people for each department. This can be particularly helpful when employees have English as their second language or when the employees can't read or write. It helps control food quantities produced, as well as save staff time. For example: Midwest City Memorial Hospital in Oklahoma has been able to reduce staff by 4½ full-time employees and reduce food costs by 6-8 percent by establishing an ingredient room. St Mary's Hospital has been able to reduce food costs by 15 to 20 percent.

- Use a timer to avoid overcooking and drying out food.

- Use a spatula to scrape bowls and cans.

- Use down time to its fullest for making croutons (preferred by most customers over purchased croutons), grating cheese to be bagged and stored in one-to-two-pound quantities for later use, and whipping butter (making the butter increase in volume and look prettier).

- Find a use for every trimming and every bone. Soups, sauces, and salsa may be made from trimmings (the imperfect slice of tomato or less tender portion of asparagus). Bread pudding is a favorite of many adults and can be made from "leftovers" or "ends" of bread, broken cookies, and cakes. One of the favorite toppings on ice cream may be made from chocolate chip cookies (the imperfect ones).

- Plan menu items like vegetable and meat-type soups, hashes, and meat pies to use leftover bits and pieces. Plan fruit cups to use the almost overripe banana, the apple with a spot, etc.

- Put someone dependable in charge of leftovers. Record what is left and how much, and plan when the leftovers will be used. Be certain the leftovers are stored and labeled immediately.

- Maintain a record of food waste and check it frequently; Wendy's and McDonald's have made this a standard daily report.

COR   • Cook/Chill—The Philadelphia Prison System has improved the average cost of meals from $1.31 to $1.18 by using cook/chill, which has allowed them to buy commodity items in bulk at more competitive prices and to better control waste. They have reduced not only food costs but labor costs as well.

Enforcing Portion Control

It is important to determine what the portion size will be and how to measure the portion, and to check frequently to ensure that the correct portion is being served. Provide utensils and equipment for portioning. See Exhibit 5.11. Portions that are measured by weight, e.g., sliced meats and cheese, require proper scales. For example, two ounces cannot be weighed on pound scales very accurately. A digital ounce-portioning set of scales will pay for itself within a week.

Consider offering "petite portions" and "hearty portions" to help reduce plate waste. Watch the quantity of waste returned on the plates--determine what you are "overdoing." If half the sour cream on the Mexican food is usually uneaten, the portion of sour cream is too large. Reduce food waste by watching "untouched" food "returns" and evaluate portion sizes by watching food returns in general. On bread, for example, put on table the portions that the number of customers can be expected to eat.

Train employees in how to portion correctly, and have rules on "freebies"--all food adds to the cost. Many foodservices have found that portion packs save money and are more sanitary, but the employees can defeat the whole purpose of portion packs if they give the customer a handful of catsup packs, for instance. Many fast-food restaurants fail to instruct their employees in how many packages to give the customer. Someone orders two servings (six each) of chicken nuggets, and the cashier gives the customer five packets of sweet and sour sauce, eight of barbecue sauce, and ten of catsup packets. The cost of the condiments (<u>added together</u>) may be 50¢ to 60¢. The food cost of twice as many condiments as needed just increased the food cost of chicken nuggets by 30¢ more than necessary. Exhibit 5.11 provides an example of what happens when the ice cream dip is rounded versus level.

Exhibit 5.11   Portion Control Keeps Costs as Planned

Dipper/ Scoop Size	Average Yield Per Gallon Ice Cream (When Level Dips)	Average Yield per Gallon Ice Cream (When Rounded Dips)	Cost Per Serving Based on $6/gal.
No. 8	30-32 dips -- approx. 2 ½ oz each	15 dips -- approx. 5 oz each	20¢ -- not 40¢
No. 10	38-40 dips -- approx. 1 7/8 oz each	19 dips -- approx. 3 3/4 oz each	15.1¢ -- not 31.5¢
No. 12	46-48 dips -- approx. 1 5/8 oz each	23 dips -- approx. 3 1/8 oz each	13.4¢ -- not 26¢
No. 16	58-62 dips -- approx. 1 1/4 oz each	29 dips -- approx. 2 ½ oz each	10.3¢ -- not 20¢

Pre-portion foods for later use. For example, Subway weighs out the meat and cheese portions ahead of time for later use when assembling the subs at rush hour. Some examples of ways to control costs follow.

SCH   • Use portion control. **Bellingham (WA) Schools'** foodservice director credits portion control for keeping the food cost under food-based menu planning at 60¢ to 70¢ per lunch (33% of revenue). (Food-based menu planning is one of the options for schools to use in their efforts to meet the USDA published Dietary Guidelines.)

ALL   • Watch food returns. Could smaller portions be provided? Question carefully before changing portion size. Commercial cafeterias, some restaurants, and college cafeterias may find the portions must be generous. It is financially disastrous to gain a reputation for serving small portions. Luby's Cafeterias, Inc., has built a reputation for serving large portions, as have many other foodservices.

         • Pre-portion during pre-preparation when pressure is not on; e.g., weigh meat and cheese for each sub sandwich, use deli paper or pan liners to separate layers, and store sub meat and cheese until needed.

         • Keep "voids" at a minimum. Voids are foods that are returned or spilled. Keep a record of portions rejected by servers and the reasons for the returns or voids and the sales value of the menu items. Evaluating this record can alert management to problems with servers or kitchen staff.

HC   • Streamline delivery of menus. The Dana-Farber Cancer Institute in Boston reduced food costs by 30% in 1995 and increased patient satisfaction with changes in how menus are provided patients in the following manner: Patients are provided with menus for breakfast, lunch, and dinner. The patient places a phone order for the items of choice at any time between 7 a.m. and 6:30 p.m. The trays are delivered within 30 minutes of the call. More than 80% of the dinner orders are phoned in between 6 and 6:30 p.m. This procedure reduced the number of undelivered trays tremendously. They went from 2.7 meal equivalents per patient day to 2.1. They discontinued maintaining nourishment centers on each of the patient floors. Instead, the next nourishment was delivered when the meal was taken to the floor.

      Food cost is one of the prime costs of foodservices, and it is very controllable. The percentage of revenue spent varies in the different segments of the foodservice industry by as much as 15-25 percent, e.g., bagel shop, 26 percent; schools, 40-50 percent (including the value of USDA commodities). Managing and controlling food costs starts at the back door (loading dock) and doesn't end until the meal is served. Food costs are variable costs and can be reduced by two to four percent in most foodservices without a reduction being noticed.

Computerization has made it possible for many foodservices to precost every meal without a lot of effort once the database is set up and updated. At the same time, recipes are extended and printed out for the exact amount.

Exhibit 5.1 provides an example of a precosted recipe, which shows the ideal cost. Exhibit 5.2 illustrates how food costs are broken down into portions or usable units, making precosting and postcosting easier. (This is a job the computer does well.)

"Doggie bags" have become a trend--indicating that portions are too large. Is this part of marketing or not intended? Doggie bags (the containers) need to be costed out and included in the food cost during the planning stages.

Planning Use of Leftovers

In many instances, food costs can be cut down by reducing and/or using leftovers more effectively. Better forecasting and following of recipes that have been extended out for the forecasted amounts can help decrease leftovers.

The menus should have some items planned that will use leftovers, e.g., vegetable-beef soup and fruit cup. Making bread pudding from leftover bread is an excellent way to use some leftovers and may be a customer favorite, too.

Many chefs have learned at culinary schools or from mentors not to throw away edible food. Management needs to evaluate how much time it takes to utilize trimmings, e.g., stalks of broccoli and all the parts of the beef quarter. It may be more cost effective to purchase the items needed already prepared and avoid the trimmings.

Deciding what to do with leftovers and trimmings requires some planning. Every management of a foodservice operation needs a policy about employees taking home leftovers and trimmings. Most foodservice operations do not allow the practice at all because it can get out of hand and can encourage "overcooking." A policy regarding leftovers should address:

- Which leftovers can be used later
- How long leftovers can be held
- How leftovers will be handled and stored
- How leftovers can be presented with a different appearance; for example, mashed potatoes can be priced higher when converted to twice-baked potatoes
- Whether employees will be allowed to take home leftovers (not recommended)

6
BREAK-EVEN POINT

CONTENTS

OBJECTIVES OF CHAPTER 6

After studying this chapter, the reader should be able to:

- Calculate the annual, weekly, and daily fixed costs
- Determine the variable costs and contribution margin
- Establish the break-even point
- Plan a profit into the break-even point
- Determine how to make the break-even point obtainable
- Use the break-even point to set goals

The break-even point (BEP) is that point in time when you have served enough customers and made enough sales to pay all of your operating costs-- before profit. Improving sales is what is needed to stay in business. The BEP can be used to identify and solve problems in regard to sales. Many new businesses start up each day that will go under by the end of the first year. If the owners/managers had only figured their BEP, they may never have opened their doors.

The BEP is a vital management tool that enables management to perform analyses on an existing operation, a potential operation, or a portion of an operation. A foodservice operation in general has so many variables that it is impossible to predetermine all of them. The BEP enables management to better see the effects that slight changes in sales, fixed costs, and/or variable costs will have on the results. It better enables management to preset the percentage of profits from the start.

Knowing the BEP is useful regardless of the type of foodservice. Wouldn't it be nice to know how many customers you need to serve to break even, and at what time of day you cover costs and begin making a profit? It is said that a well-managed McDonald's covers fixed costs by 10 a.m., and from then on a percentage of every dollar taken in is profit.

The **BEP is the point at which the sales--or revenue--equal the expenses.** At this point there is no profit or loss, and thereafter any additional revenues taken in or received contain some profit. BEP analyses will tell a manager how many dollars in sales are needed to break even, and by dividing the dollars by the average customer check, the number of customers needed can be arrived at. For example, if the daily BEP is $825 and the average check size is $3.49, divide $825 by $3.49:

$$\$825 \div \$3.49 = 237 \text{ customers}$$

As another example, a restaurant's rent is $1,500 per month, a loan at the bank for startup costs, $700 per month, liability/hazard insurance, $120 per month, and the manager's salary with fringe benefits, $60,000 per year or $5,000 per month; these are all fixed costs.

BREAK-EVEN POINT FORMULA

BEP analysis is a cost accountant's tool made easy by using a mathematical formula as shown in this chapter. Mathematical formulas scare some, but that shouldn't happen in this case. If one follows the formula and does what the formula says, the BEP can be arrived at quickly and easily.

$$\frac{\text{Fixed Costs \$}\rule{3cm}{0.4pt}}{100\% - \text{Variable Costs \%} = \text{Contribution Margin \%}} = \text{BEP \$}\rule{2cm}{0.4pt}$$

The BEP occurs when enough sales are made to pay for food, supplies, labor, and all overhead. To perform the BEP analysis, you need two pieces of information: fixed costs in dollars and variable costs as percentage of revenue. The first step is to determine which costs are fixed and which are variable.

Determining Fixed Costs

Fixed costs are the costs that do not vary from day to day dependent on the volume of sales. Fixed costs remain constant over time or may even go up (e.g., liability insurance goes up nationwide). Fixed costs almost never start at zero because some fixed costs are involved with just operating. On the other hand, revenue may start at zero, as do variable costs.

Fixed costs are shown in dollar amounts--these are known amounts. These costs should be identifiable amounts. Many foodservice operators do not know what their fixed costs are, but need to know. These are important costs to identify, because there is no profit to be made until fixed costs and variable costs have been paid.

The unit manager may have little control over fixed costs--these may be established by upper management, stockholders, civil service ratings and classifications, or school boards.

Definition:

Fixed costs--those costs that do not vary with day-to-day or week-to-week volumes of sales or numbers of customers served.

     Examples:
     Rent
     Insurance
     Loan payment/depreciation
     Telephone basic charges
     Management salaries/fringe benefits
     Core staff salaries (number essential to being open for business)
     Marketing/advertising[1]
     Other
     Depreciation

Fixed costs are expressed in dollar amounts and remain fairly constant.

Determining Variable Costs

The second piece of information needed is variable costs, those costs that increase or decrease in direct proportion to sales. Since variable costs fluctuate, they are expressed in percentages (percentage of costs to revenue).

Definition:

Variable costs--those costs that vary in direct proportion to volume of sales or numbers of customers served. Variable costs may differ for different types of service (e.g., in a hospital food costs for the executive dining room may be higher than for the tray service patients). Some of the costs that generally vary in direct proportion to volume are:

     Food and supplies
     Part-time and/or substitute labor
     Franchise fee or profit if expressed in percentage
     Utilities
     Maintenance

---

[1]May be considered variable.

To determine variable costs, it helps to have last year's or last month's financial statement to determine what percentage of the revenue was spent for the items that you determined vary from day to day based on volume of business. To determine the percentage, divide the costs by the total revenue.

Note that the unit manager can have a lot of influence over variable costs. For example, if there has been a big snow and the roads are impassable, management would bring in fewer part-time employees and prepare ahead for fewer customers.

Determining the Contribution Margin

The third piece of information needed to determine the BEP is the contribution margin. To determine the contribution margin, subtract the total variable costs in percentages from the revenue represented by 100%.

Definition:

Contribution margin--that portion of the revenue left once the variable costs have been covered. This revenue is sometimes referred to as the "gross profit." It is the percent of the revenue that can be used to pay the fixed costs, and once fixed costs are paid, the contribution margin is the percentage of each dollar in sales that is profit.

The contribution margin is the percentage of the revenue left after variable costs are paid. Total revenues, or total sales, are expressed as 100% in the BEP formula. Once variable costs--food, supplies, and part-time labor, which are expressed in percentages-- are subtracted from the sales (100%), the percentage left from sales goes toward paying for fixed costs.

Is it possible to break even (cover costs) in "X" location? And make a profit? Should you open for breakfast? Will you make money at breakfast or would your costs be greater than your additional revenue? It may not be physically possible to bring in enough revenue to cover the costs. The BEP analysis helps management to spot and solve problems in existing operations.

The formula for obtaining the contribution margin is as follows:

<u>100% (represents revenue)</u> minus <u>variable costs (%)</u>   =   <u>contribution margin (%)</u>

DETERMINING THE BREAK-EVEN POINT

With the three pieces of information--fixed costs in dollars, variable costs in percentages, and the contribution margin in percentage--converted to decimals (e.g., 47% = .47), the BEP--how many dollars of revenue are needed--can be determined.

The formula to use is:

Fixed cost/month ($)   =   **$**
Contribution margin ____   **BEP/month**

BEP ÷ Average Number Operating Days per Month per Month = Daily BEP

The BEP may be determined by the year or the month; however, it helps to break it down to a daily amount. This can be done by dividing the average annual or month's expenses by the average number of days when there were sales.

The average daily revenue should be compared with the average daily BEP. To do this, divide the annual revenue/sales by the number of days of service during the year or the average monthly revenue by the number of days of operation. For example, in Exhibit 6.1, the BEP formula can help determine if the manager can make a profit. J. Smith has just purchased a coffee shop, Java Shop, which was just about to go under. Java can seat 32 people. It is open for business six days a week and is grossing $360 a day. The question is, "How much does J. Smith need to gross each day to break even?"

First, Java's monthly expenses are listed for fixed costs. These costs include rent, lease or loan payment, utilities, and wages of salaried employees. J. Smith pays himself a salary--this salary will be a fixed cost. Add the fixed costs together for the total fixed cost. These are costs that will not vary from day to day.

Second, the average monthly variable costs--those costs which vary from day to day depending upon the volume of sales--should be determined. These include food, paper supplies, detergents, part-time employees, franchise fees or profits (that vary with the volume of sales), and credit-card charges. Since these costs vary, they are shown in percentages. These variable costs should be added together.

Once the variable costs have been arrived at, the contribution margin can be determined. This is done by subtracting the total variable costs in percentages from the total revenue represented by 100%. The percentage of revenue left after variable costs are paid is the contribution margin.

With this information the BEP can be determined. The total fixed costs should be divided by the contribution margin (expressed in decimals, e.g., 43% = .43). The daily BEP can be arrived at by dividing the month by the number of days the Java Shop is open for business. Exhibit 6.1 shows the details of the Java Shop's BEP.

Exhibit 6.1 Sample of the Java Shop's BEP for Month in Detail

Monthly Costs	Dollars & Percentage of Revenue	Fixed Costs	Variable Costs
Labor	$ 3,300	$3,300	
Payroll Tax	366	366	
Part-Time Employee Wages	7.4%		7.4%
Food/Beverages	25.4%		25.4%
Paper Supplies	3.7%		3.7%
Detergents/Other	2.2%		2.2%
Rent	$ 700	700	
Insurance	80	80	
Telephone	95	95	
Depreciation	100	100	
Utilities	300	300	
Advertising/Marketing	60	60	
Franchise Fee	212	212	
Miscellaneous	80	80	
Accountant Services	100	100	
TOTALS		$5,293	38.7%

The total fixed cost is $5,293 per month, and the variable costs equal 38.7% of the sales/revenue.

100% Revenue - 38.7% Variable Costs   =   61.3% Contribution Margin

Out of every dollar of sales, 61.3%, or $.613 (61.3¢), goes toward paying fixed costs. After fixed costs have been covered, 61.3¢ out of every dollar of sales becomes profit.

To determine the BEP, divide the fixed costs by the contribution margin, as shown below:

  $5,293 Fixed Costs   = $8,635 BEP for a Month
.613 Contribution Margin

The Java Shop has average sales of $340 per day and is open an average of 26 days per month. The BEP is $8,640 for a month.

$8,635 BEP for month ÷ 26 days open   = $332 BEP per day

The Java Shop has a very small profit of $8 per day or $208 per month ($340 - $332 = $8 X 26 = $208). If the owner wants more profits, the manager will have to reduce costs or increase sales. How would you reduce costs? How would you increase the sales? This will be discussed more later in this chapter.

INCLUDING A PROFIT IN THE BREAK-EVEN POINT

If the owner and/or management's goal is to make a profit (a specific amount), the profit should be planned. To help ensure there is a profit, the desired profit margin should be added into the BEP formula. Regardless of the type of operation--commercial or noncommercial--a profit is usually desired.

There are two ways of including the profit margin in the BEP formula: (1) as a percentage of the sales (add percentage of profit to variable cost) or (2) as a dollar amount (add profit in dollars to fixed costs).

DETERMINING HOW TO SOLVE THE PROBLEM

If the revenue falls short of the BEP, or if the profit is not sufficient for the owner(s), there are three ways of correcting the problem:

1. Reduce variable costs, usually the easiest of the three options.

2. Reduce fixed costs, which would mean management may have to make major changes in the operation--reduce the number of salaried positions, negotiate the lease down, etc.

3. Increase revenue by increasing the customer count, e.g., opening for breakfast, increasing the customer's check (amount spent), or adding other services. Increasing revenue or sales will not yield the profits that reducing costs will.

When the revenue is not adequate or the costs are too high, the following steps can be used in solving the problem.

Reducing Variable Costs

Before attempting to reduce variable costs, compare the variable costs with the industry standards provided in Chapters 4 and 5. Remember, the goal is to keep food costs within the industry level: restaurants/fast-food establishments, 28%-34%, colleges/universities, 32%-34%, schools, 35%-40%, and hospitals, 35%.

Variable costs are controlled by unit managers and are usually the easiest to decrease. Food costs make up the largest share of the variable costs, and food waste can usually be reduced by 1% to 2% easily and without a lot of negative effects.

In the case of the coffee shop, the manager needs to check other coffee shops to determine what is a reasonable food cost. If the existing food cost appears to be low, it may not be possible to reduce that cost. By reducing food costs only 2%, the profits in the above case would be increased to $278 per month. Since the food costs are already low, there may not be much waste and a 2% decrease may not be possible.

See Chapters 4 and 5 for suggestions for reducing labor and food costs. Once a decrease has been established, re-figure the BEP. After each change, re-figure the BEP again to see if the desired effect has been obtained.

Decreasing Fixed Costs

Fixed costs are not as easy to reduce as variable costs; however, they can be decreased. Each cost should be questioned to determine which can be reduced. A little each day will make a difference. Check industry averages in the area. Question all costs. For example, can the labor costs or fringe benefits be reduced? Can more of the labor costs be classified as "variable costs" instead of fixed costs? Can advertising/marketing or telephone costs be reduced? Could management do its own payroll and reduce the accountant fees to just the cost of preparing end-of-year taxes? None of these may be easy solutions or the remedy desired.

Fixed costs, sometimes referred to as "uncontrollable costs," are controlled by upper management and aren't as easy to reduce because labor makes up the largest share of the costs. Management occasionally adopts the attitude that fixed costs can't be reduced, which is not true. The idea that fixed costs are "uncontrollable" is often an excuse for management not taking control of the more difficult areas--and make changes. Union contracts, rent/lease/ insurance, and upper management's salaries often fall into this category. Union contract changes (concessions) do take negotiations with management (give up something to get something). Rent/leases can be re-negotiated and often changed. And, if need be, the location can be changed.

Upper management's salaries get out of proportion and control when things are going well. It may be necessary to lower the number of executives and/or their salaries. Another solution may be to establish a base salary and add bonuses that are tied to profits. Chapter 4 addresses some other ways of reducing fixed labor costs. The BEP should be re-figured after each decrease in fixed costs.

Increasing Revenue

When the goal is to increase revenue, management will want to determine if the prices charged are too low. To determine if they are, management can check what competitors are charging and check the true costs (precost and postcost) of each item to see if the profit margin is adequate.

Other ways of increasing revenue can be considered. For example, the Java Shop may wish to add some new menu items or add another service, e.g., offering for sale some of the popular morning newspapers, e.g., *USA Today* or *Wall Street Journal*.

Revenue increases may or may not be an easy way of improving the situation. Usually revenue can be increased with creative marketing and innovative new ways of generating sales.

Increasing revenue will be an effective way of increasing the profits only if fixed costs do not increase at the same time.

It may take a combination of **decreasing fixed and variable costs and increasing revenue** to break even or make the desired profits. It will depend on how tightly operated the foodservice operation is and how saturated the market is.

The BEF analyses should be run before increasing the use of convenience foods and subcontracting with other foodservices to provide parts of the menus, e.g., a university bringing in Subway sandwiches for resale--"What is the BEP?" The variable costs (food costs) usually increase substantially. The question becomes, will fixed costs (labor costs) be reduced? If not, the overall costs will increase.

Determining if It Is Possible to Break Even

It may not be possible to break even because the customer base isn't large enough to support the overhead costs. Costs can be reduced just so much. The BEP formula is especially useful to run before purchasing/opening up a new restaurant. It should be a part of a feasibility study.

The BEP is helpful to foodservice directors of health care units, schools, and universities/colleges. The BEP analyses will tell the directors if a specific unit is profitable or if it is possible to make it profitable. The BEP will bring the problem to the attention of upper management, which usually controls fixed costs. Companies that are "downsizing" (reducing size of staff and/or physical plants) are reducing fixed costs. Today downsizing has become a common occurrence.

USING THE BEP TO MOTIVATE EMPLOYEES

Reaching the BEP can be a motivator to management and employees if broken down into goals. The next step after determining the BEP is to determine if the revenue is sufficient to reach the BEP. If the revenue is not sufficient, break down the difference in expenditures, revenue, and BEP to a daily amount, which makes it easier to see the problem. For example, if the variable costs exceed 50%, it will be nearly impossible to break even, and the variable costs need to be reduced. The question becomes, "how much should variable costs be decreased each day?" If increasing revenue has been set as a goal, how much does the revenue need to be increased per day? E.g., $200 per month or $200 ÷ 24 days (in the case of the Java Shop) = $8.34 per day. The goals can be broken down further--to hours of day or by employee.

The BEP formula makes the problems easier to understand, and the formula enables one to see problems and visually see results from minor changes in variable and fixed costs. The formula can tell a new manager what the outcome will be before it is too late to take corrective action. Michael J. Stausser, president of Economic Consulting Associates, calls the BEP formula a magic formula, and many agree with him.

The BEP can be translated into goals--increases in revenue for breakfast, lunch, or dinner; decreases in costs. Managers can ask for the help of the staff by informing the staff of the problems and giving each staff member a goal. For example, if the Java Shop's manager had to increase profits from $8 per day to $20 per day, the increase could be divided into an amount for breakfast and for lunch. If there were more than one point-of-sale unit, the increases could be divided among those cashiers. Or, J. Smith may decide that it would take a combination of decreasing costs and increasing sales. Breaking down the goals to smaller parts can often help in accomplishing the goals.

Similar units need to compare their respective break-even points. Comparison, setting goals, and checking results cannot be overemphasized as motivators for managers.

7
USING TECHNOLOGY
IN CONTROLLING COSTS

CONTENTS

OBJECTIVES OF CHAPTER 7

After studying this chapter, the reader should be able to:

- Briefly discuss the advantages of computerizing
- Identify the areas that can be computerized
- Identify the steps to preparing the back of the house for computerization
- List at least five cost-related functions that can be computerized
- Describe how spreadsheets can be used to computerize different functions
- Recognize how technology can be used to help control costs

Technology has had a noticeable impact on most businesses in the last decade. Many businesses, and even individuals in their homes, are using the fax machine and internet as ways of obtaining and dispensing information. The computer chip can be found in many pieces of equipment today.

For years the foodservice industry has been manually oriented and labor-intensive. The self-operated/self-managed segments of the foodservice industry lack standardization, and that's one of the main reasons for the high casualty rates among new restaurant owners. Some chefs and cooks "do their own thing" and carry their menus and recipes with them. Sometimes those recipes are in their heads, making it impossible to computerize or duplicate them. Computerization requires written recipes and standardization, which is one of the biggest pluses to computerizing any foodservice operation.

ADVANTAGES OF COMPUTERIZING

A computerized system should yield concrete benefits, such as:

- Improved accuracy
- Reduction in time required
- Improved response time
- Better information provided
- Improved integrity of information
- Required standardization
- Improved security

These are benefits that may not occur in the first month of operation--or in several months--but that will occur. Foodservice needs to be approached more as an exact science. Today controls are essential to a successful food operation when competition is so great. The computer makes it possible to develop the "exact science" part of operating a foodservice.

Foodservice operations that have computerized from the back door (receiving the food) to the front door (service) are realizing many pluses. Bob Kilgore of The CBORD Group said, "These foodservices are typically producing better, more consistent products at significantly less cost than their manually operated counterparts."[1]   Marriott is scheduling labor using

---

[1]Bakos, *Handbook of Noncommercial Foodservice Management.*

software to help increase productivity and decrease labor costs, which will yield cost savings for years to come.

There can be dangers and disadvantages to computerization, however, when management becomes too dependent upon the computer.

FUNCTIONS TO COMPUTERIZE

Computerization goes hand in hand with cost control, and the data is available to identify, break down, and analyze the costs. The categories of computing that can be used in foodservices are:

1. Word processing
2. Data processing
3. Logical processing
4. Mathematical calculations
5. Communication
6. Design

The functions in a foodservice operation that influence costs and that the computer does well are:

- Point-of-sale functions

- Menu planning with preference data

- Menu planning within cost restraints and meeting nutritional requirements

- Recipe extensions

- Recipe and menu precosting and postcosting

- Forecasting and ordering

- Bid analyses

- Perpetual and physical inventories

- Production records

- Production planning

- Scheduling of employees

- Payroll, time and attendance

- Payment of invoices and billing for services

- Equipment inventory and preventive maintenance records

- Depreciation

- Budget planning, analyzing, and evaluating

- Financial records and reports

- "What-if" ability

- Communicating information quickly, e.g., hospital patient status

There is probably no other industry that needs computerization more than the foodservice industry. This is very evident when one looks at the list of complex jobs above. Stand-alone systems that do just one of the above functions should be avoided. An integrated system that eventually computerizes all departments within the operation is by far the most desirable--indeed essential--although it may not be financially feasible or advisable to totally computerize the operation all at the same time.

Selecting the best hardware and software packages is complex and confusing. There are a number of resources to turn to, such as: *1997 Director of Computer Hardware and Software for the Foodservice Industry*, published by the National Restaurant Association; the 1997 *Annual Journal of Dietetic Software*, and the *Computer Programs and Databases in the Field of Nutrition*, published by Computer Information Center at the University of Washington; United States Department of Agriculture (USDA) approved list of software for nutrient analysis and a detailed food database.

There are many sources of computerized, standardized recipes, which can save tremendous time--for example, CBORD, Inc., has databases for many popular recipe books, such as, *Food for Fifty, Wenzel's Menu Maker*,

Standardized Recipe File for Quantity and Quality from Iowa State University, and others.

TOTAL MANAGEMENT INFORMATION SYSTEM

A management information system is defined as collecting, processing, storing, and disseminating information. A total management system approach that is integrated and can accomplish all the functions listed is recommended. It may be difficult to find a ready-made management information system that will fit all existing foodservice needs. It is often necessary to tailor the system to an operation, which can be expensive. There are some "stand- alone" modules, e.g., a nutritional analysis package. The question is, will it interface with the back-of-house software, the inventory system? If it won't, it means having to create a food file and recipe file again.

POINT-OF-SALE SYSTEM

One of the best definitions for a point-of-sale (POS) system is that it is "a computer that thinks it's a cash register." POS registers provide a lot more than just record-keeping and sales analyses. They are more than the electronic cash register (ECR), which is a cash handling device. POS registers may stand alone (are considered "dumb" terminals), but most are "intelligent." All kinds of valuable information can be obtained from the communicating POS that is connected with the central computer.

The ideal is for the POS to push the back of the house--a meal sold reorders and establishes the size of production needed. Such a system can track history, patrons by day and by menu, number of guests served by each server, average sales per customer, and sales in a given time frame, and perform many more functions.

Computers also play a role in marketing, and this area will be enhanced in the future by the internet. POS TV monitors running food advertisements or menu selections on laser disk will take orders by a touch of the screen by the customer. The video screen will verify the order with how much the check is.

Universities and colleges use some of the most sophisticated point-of-sale systems. For example, the University of Georgia uses a biometrics access system for the contract dining halls that uses three-dimensional hand print and gets students in the door in less than three seconds. The system is so sensitive that a change in the ring the student is wearing will make a difference in recognition.

The debit cards which draw from funds deposited by the customers (or maybe against the employee's payroll) are frequently used by universities, schools, and B&Is. The smart card is a type of debit card that has many uses, including use in vending machines.

Today in most restaurants the waitstaffs use a computer terminal to place orders with the kitchen, print out the tab, and begin the process of accountability. Theft has become more difficult with the detailed accountability possible. The amount of data and the ways it can be analyzed are endless.

BACK-OF-HOUSE MANAGEMENT SYSTEM

Preparing for computerization is time-consuming--but the side benefits cannot be over-praised. In order to computerize back of the house, the foodservice operation has to use standardize procedures--foremost is creating a food file and having standardized recipes and portion control.

There is so much to be computerized in back of the house that it is hard to know where to start. Taking one step at a time, the back of the house can be computerized and networked together if one system contains all the programs and utilizes the same database. The food database requires a lot of information, and the accuracy is essential to nutrient analysis and costing of recipes and menus.

Electronic data processing makes it possible to tabulate the hundreds of bits of data necessary to control the back of the house. The first essential to controlling the back of the house is the standardized recipe file. Some of the finer restaurants depend entirely on "the chef's" memory--when the chef or the memory goes, too often the quality of the food goes or changes.

The computer will decide what should be issued from stock based on (1) the menu, (2) amount forecasted, and (3) recipe-specified ingredients. The nutritional analyses and costing of the menus planned and served can be run from the data in the system.

Production records, scheduling of employees, time analyses, labor productivity, and cost analyses are important, time-consuming tasks that can be handled by computer.

Menu Planning and Nutrient Analyses

Computer-assisted menu planning (CAMP) is one of the oldest computer programs used for menu planning, but it has had not-so-successful results (as well as success stories) as management has learned that menu planning is a complex process that even computers have trouble executing. Management usually plans the menu, then checks it on the computer for cost and nutrient content, and then adjusts accordingly, with a person doing much of the decision process. However, there are other menu planning programs interactively involving management in the planning process that also work.

Computer programs can plan menus that conform to diets prescribed quite well, and in less than 20 percent of the time this would take to analyze diets manually. There are numerous databases, and which one to use becomes a question--some are limited and have incorrect data or are limited in what they will do. The United States Department of Agriculture (USDA) has reviewed and approved the computerized software that will adequately analyze the school menus, and the schools are limited to those programs that have USDA approval.

Computerized Purchasing/Electronic Commerce

The bid process is easy to computerize and can be more accurately evaluated with the use of computers. It also provides the ability to establish the most economical approach to purchasing--whether that be the "one-stop" purchasing option (purchasing all from one vendor) or "cherry picking" (purchasing by line item from several vendors based on the best price).

Shopping through the internet is a growing trend in the foodservice industry. Companies are seeing the value of using the internet as a marketing tool. A manager can place an order (after shopping around), pay for the order, arrange delivery, pull the product from the company's inventory, and add it to the foodservices' inventory through the use of the internet.

Obtaining price quotes weekly for produce and analyzing the quotes/quantities can be done in a fraction of the time it took in the past. Because the process has a fast turnaround, it is possible to bid more frequently and closer to the time of delivery. Again, obtaining prices quickly has been improved through the use of E-mail or even the more manual approach, the fax machine.

Once the vendor is selected, the purchase orders can be automatically produced, the vendor's inventory accessed, and orders placed directly on the computer and transmitted to the vendor in minutes. The flowchart for forecasting in Chapter 5 shows how simple computerizing the forecasting and ordering process can be.

Suppliers can present their information about new products and services via storefronts in an on-line shopping mall. This not only can change the role of sales representatives, it can save time and money. According to the February 1998 *Profit Magazine*, the software Oracle Applications Release II automates procurement with workflow technology.

On-line catalogs enable managers to find product information (and other up-to-date information) about many products. A foodservice director can load the entire product offerings of its major suppliers. Product support is available on a few products; soon it will be on many. Orders can be tracked regarding shipping status. The University of Pennsylvania Acquisition Services is using the Oracle Applications Purchasing module to advance its ability to shop around and save time.

Electronic commerce has made ordering, tracking, receiving, and paying invoices easy. Data entry can be greatly reduced. With the Web, managers won't need company equipment catalogs because the products will be on line.

With the click of a computer mouse and the use of electronic commerce, a customer can place orders, pay for products, reduce inventory, arrange delivery, and have inventory replaced without any human interaction.

The 1998 Conference of Healthcare EDI Coalition included sessions on E-Commerce and strategies for providing supply-chain efficiency.

Inventory Control

Perpetual inventory, as well as physical inventory, can become paperless with the use of bar code readers and a hand-held terminal unit that is connected to an integrated system. The perpetual inventory process that became too expensive to do in the late 1970s may now be maintained efficiently and accurately.

"PAR" stock levels of inventory (the minimum amount that should always be in stock) can be monitored and orders automatically placed when the levels indicate--all by computer. However, PAR stock level philosophy tends to encourage higher inventory than is necessary--some stock just "waits" to be used.

With computerization it makes more sense to adopt the just-in-time (JIT) philosophy rather than "too much because I'd rather be safe" philosophy. The menu plan for next week should be the driver of the system and determine what is ordered.

If the computer system is totally integrated, the removal of items from inventory takes place when the menus and forecasted numbers are established. The removal of items from inventory drives the ordering, which can be communicated directly to the vendor.

Physical inventory becomes a much simpler process when computerized, and particularly when the bar code technology is used. Laser beams make it possible to inventory those cases of items on the top shelf without ever stepping on a ladder.

Recipe Extension

Properly extended recipes will reduce costs and provide cooks with the ingredients and directions needed to control portion sizes and food costs, but often neither management nor the cook has the time or ability to extend the recipe according to need.

The production part of the operation is very complex and, if done in a business manner, requires volumes of calculations and detailed planning and scheduling. The computer will compute the yield of a recipe, which is useful when standardizing recipes.

Computerizing the back of the house begins with menus and standardized recipes for every item on the menu, and the food ingredients database (food or inventory file). There are many computer systems available today that have complete food inventory files, and this makes the computerization process go faster.

Precosting and Postcosting

Precosting and postcosting can be time-consuming if done manually and not done by computer, but yet these are cost-control measures that each foodservice operation needs. It is imperative that the inventory file or food file have the most current bid prices for the results to be meaningful. The precosting of recipes and menus occurs during the planning stages, and the postcosting occurs after the food has been served.

Precosting lets management know if a recipe/menu can be afforded before it is prepared and served. If the computer program is totally integrated, the menu planned becomes the first step to controlling costs.

Tray Assembly and Service

Tray assemblies in hospitals often depend on the complete menu processing system to print out the patient's selections on a ticket that becomes the driver of the tray assembly lines. It is even possible to measure the nutrients in the portions selected by a patient by just entering the menu selections into the computer system.

Patients' checkouts are updated immediately upon entry of the data into print the invoice, and this can reduce waste tremendously.

COMPUTERIZED ACCOUNTING SYSTEM

A computerized accounting system can perform all the bookkeeping chores and provide management with the needed analyses of data, such as:

- Employee time records

- Payroll

- Employer taxes

- Accounts payable and accounts receivable

- Invoicing

- Profit and loss statements (income statements)

- Balance sheet

One could easily get buried by the stacks and stacks of paper that these bookkeeping activities can generate. The important thing the computer system should provide is analyses of P & L statements and other reports for the managers and directors .

Evaluating the Use of Data

In the future, financial management will have a higher degree of accuracy, be more timely and labor-efficient, and be illustrated more dramatically--if the operation is computerized. The saying goes that "information is power," and management of any operation must have information in the future if they are to compete with those who do have information. Competition has made the margin between profit and loss so narrow that guessing won't work.

It is wise to measure the value of information and determine if all information generated is being used and is needed. Too much information can waste management's time.

Electronic Spreadsheet

If money is not available to purchase an integrated multi-program system of operation, but the company does have a computer, a spreadsheet-type software, like Lotus 1-2-3 or Excel, will be invaluable. It will not be the integrated program desired, but it will do the job.

Even a novice can set up templates with the publication by Warren Sackler and Samuel Trapani, *Foodservice Cost Control Using Microsoft Excel for Windows* (and another for Lotus 1,2,3) and run the following:

- Income statement or P&L--with percentage of sales or revenue comparison with previous month and year

- A budget--with percentage comparison with previous year's budget ready for evaluating variances from month to month to ensure the target is met

- Point-of-sale analyses, sales analyses by time of day and by menu item to determine the popularity of menu item

- Cashier's report, bank deposit, and bank statement reconciliation

- Receiving report

- Inventory control and inventory turnover

- Prorate overhead cost

- Precost and postcost of recipes and menus

- Extended recipes

- Scheduling of staff

The secret is to make templates and create an ingredient list with all the basic information needed and copy it onto the different spreadsheets.

REPORTS ON DEMAND

Management can be overwhelmed by the stack of reports being produced, and the printing of these reports takes time and incurs unnecessary costs if the reports are not being used. For example, at one facility management printed a detail of the services for the day when a summary would have provided the needed information. The types of reports desired should be scheduled as needed.

An intelligent time clock that is connected with the integrated system can regulate labor scheduling for the most cost-effective outcome. Clocking in and clocking out can be connected to payroll. How well one programs the software (with the restraints of the system) will determine how regulated it is.

"Demand reports" are generated when management requests reports. "Exception reports" are produced when something outside the parameters occurs. Analytical reports are summary-type reports with benchmarks that enable management to scan and spot problems and trends quickly.

OTHER USES OF TECHNOLOGY

The equipment manufacturers in this country have been slow to use technology because the sale of "what we've always had" has been so good. There have been small steps toward the use of technology, but the surface has just been scratched.

The many repetitious jobs in the foodservice industry lend themselves to the use of robotics and automation, but due to the cost not many have been able to adventure into the testing of new technology. Major chain restaurants like McDonald's will lead the way--we can hope.

There are many side jobs that have to be done, such as scheduling use of dining rooms/meeting rooms, that can be handled well by computer. Room service and ordering at the table can be done quite successfully by computer. The personal touch of a waitperson will never be replaced by technology, but there are times when speed is more important.

Bar Code Technology

Bar code technology has reduced the cost of entering data and has improved accuracy. The universal product code (UPC) and code 39 have become standards, particularly in the grocery and distributor areas and the health industry, with paper suppliers, and for many others.

According to Kaud in *Effective Computer Management in Food and Nutrition Services* (Aspen Publishers, Inc.), the universal product code can do the following cost-related jobs in a foodservice department or operation:

- Improve receiving

- Provide more accurate inventory control

- Improve turnaround time between order placement and delivery

- Provide analyses of product movement

These abilities not only provide speed, but foster higher productively rates and lower material handling costs.

The Health Care Industry UPN (Universal Product Number) Initiative has set a goal of industry-wide use of UPN by July 1999. The UPN is the industry-accepted key reference to product information and is a standard bar code label on all products at each unit of inventory. The U.S. Department of Health and Human Services is pushing for regulations requiring standard electronic health care transactions by the year 2000. It would be reasonable to expect all the other segments of the industry to follow the lead.

Robotics and Automation

One manager said her dream was for a robot to handle the deep fryer-- determine when the product is done, take it to the place of service, and if in a cafeteria, speak to the customer in a friendly tone. There are so many possibilities for robotics use in the kitchen, particularly in the cleanup, that robotics are bound to flourish in the near future.

Automation has made some inroads--consider the food slicer that the operator pushed back and forth and the gravity feed slicer that followed. The use of conveyor lines in large production kitchens has great potential--if there are more than 100 servings to be prepared and there are several steps, a conveyor (short) can reduce the time it takes to do the job. The cost is minimal, and the savings will pay the costs in a short time. The future use of robotics and automation will make these attempts at automation look unimportant.

Fax Machines

The fax machine seems like "old stuff" to many--within the last ten years millions of these machines have been added to the essential list of any office. With the fax machine, weekly produce price quotes are no problem, trips by an individual to pick up an order are no longer necessary, communications can be waiting for the office staff when they arrive, and there are many other usages.

Web Site and Internet

A new means of advertising is the web site. For example, the University of Georgia's menu and other information can be accessed by logging on the Food Services Home Page on the World Wide Web at www.uga.edu/food-serv. Many restaurants and universities are using their web pages to advertise the offerings.

Some definitions that may be useful at this point are as follows:

Intranet--A communication business application used within a business.

Extranet--A communication business application used in related businesses--e.g., vendors, suppliers, distributors.

Internet--Connector of the communication business applications with anywhere in the world.

A world of information is available through the internet if one has the time to research it. E-mail has become the way for upper management to communicate (without the personal interface). The time spent (or saved) has to be carefully analyzed to determine if there are any cost savings.

According to Nielsen Media Research in New York, in late 1997 more than 60 million people/companies were using the internet, and the numbers are growing daily.

The foodservice industry, the customer, and the world in which we live have changed dramatically since 1960. Chain restaurants have led the way in the foodservice industry, while some segments of the industry have lagged behind and changed very little. If today's operators do not take action, someone else will. There is a saying, "If we always do what we have always done we will get what we have always gotten." It is true in this changing world, but rather, " If foodservice management continues to like what they did in the 1960s or 1970s, they won't be able to compete in the year 2000 and beyond."

Somebody will make changes in foodservices, and it's going to be incredibly pathetic if it has to be management companies that do it. Management jeopardizes the future of the operations if it clings to old assumptions and expectations about how foodservices should operate.

The award of operating foodservices tomorrow will go to those who catch on to what's happening--those who invest their energy in finding and seizing the opportunities brought about by change.

8
TRENDS THAT COULD AFFECT COSTS

CONTENTS

OBJECTIVES OF CHAPTER 8

After studying this chapter, the reader should be able to:

- Identify some trends that could affect costs
- Identify areas where expansion in services will occur
- Foresee the effects of tighter budgets on some segments of the industry
- Determine how labor shortages and diversities will effect costs
- Identify other trends that could affect costs

Trends may be the "handwriting on the wall" that indicates when increases in costs are about to occur--or, when it may be possible to reduce costs. We can't predict the future with any accuracy because of the pace of change; however, trends do give us warning signs of what may occur. Jack Welch, General Electric CEO, tells us in his book, *Control Your Destiny or Somebody Else Will*, that change is natural and constant, continuity is unnatural, but change does not happen at random.

There are a number of predictions of changes that may help the foodservice industry and others that will have negative effects. Several will be discussed in this chapter.

EXPANSION OF SERVICES

Offerings by foodservices will be expanded because of several predictions, such as increases in population, increases in day care centers for children and the elderly, increases in shelters for homeless children, and more meals eaten outside the home than ever before.

A recent report by the NYD Group, a Port Washington (New York) market research firm, showed that more meals are being eaten outside the home today than ever before. "Takeout" is the fastest growing trend today in the foodservice business. The Group reports that there were more restaurant meals eaten off-site than on premises in 1996. According to the United States Department of Agriculture, only 53 percent of the money spent on food today is at the grocery store.

To counteract this decrease in cooking at home, grocery stores have responded with "partially prepared" items that are ready to finish off at home. Deli departments have expanded, and chefs now prepare foods in front of the customers to take home. Also, restaurants are popping up inside some grocery stores.

Home meal replacement (HMR), a new terminology, is the biggest growing market, and it will have as great an impact on the next decade as branding (selling known brands of food) did on this decade. HMR is different from take out, which is ready to eat. HMR food is replacing food made at home from scratch and other less convenient foods.

Some have taken HMR a step further and offer catered-at-home meals. This enables people to entertain at home with convenience and work-free meal/service.

Even hospitals and B&I foodservices are preparing take-home items. The University of Georgia and many other universities and colleges sell "tailgate" meals ready for pickup before big football games. These are some of the innovative ways in which the industry is responding to customers.

Foodservice Management Branching Out

Foodservice operations are using lobbies and waiting areas to branch out into the sales of items other than food. Selling T-shirts at Hard Rock Cafes in many parts of the world and selling gifts at Cracker Barrel (gift wrapped) has become big business for these foodservices as well as many others as they become known for their gift shops, jewelry sales, cookbooks, bakery take-home goods, and other specialty items.

B&Is have added services like laundries, gift stores, dry cleaning, shoe repair service, film developing drop-off, and off-site catering. Universities and colleges have thought of items for every occasion to be sold in their convenience stores.

TIGHTER BUDGETS AND INCREASED COMPETITION

Tighter budgets are being seen among all segments of the foodservice industry. The noncommercial segments of the industry are being the hardest hit and are responding with major changes in operations.

Less Financial Support

Less financial support is being experienced by the nonprofit segments of the foodservice industry. More foodservices are expected to be self-supporting operations, e.g., less company subsidy for B&Is, less support for university/college foodservices, and less local support for public schools.

Fewer B&Is are subsidizing the foodservice operation. The number of B&Is being subsidized has decreased. The average for those being subsidized is approximately $250 per employee a year. Some self-operated B&Is are expected to yield a profit.

Foodservice operations are being expected to be a source of revenue for industries, schools, hospitals, etc. This is a trend that will grow as buildings become more in need of repair and replacement. Many universities discontinued subsidizing their foodservices years ago.

Management Being Made More Responsible

Managers/directors and department heads are being held more responsible for the bottom line, particularly in hospitals and nursing homes. When management does not produce a positive bottom line management is likely to be removed from the position. This has been a way of life for the commercial industry for years, but now it is a trend in the noncommercial areas as well. Universities, colleges, B&Is, hospitals, and schools are going outside for management when there are promises of a better bottom line.

LABOR FORCE CHANGES

Labor force shortages and diversities are trends that began to be noticed as major factors in how jobs were accomplished about five years ago. This is in part because of the large number of retirements expected in the late 1990s and early 2000s. English as a second language becomes a situation to deal with as new immigrants continue to come to this country and fill the increasing need for service labor. They come with a willing to work attitude, and they are a source of dependable and "cheap" labor.

Universities and colleges are having to make major changes as shortages of student labor and the minimum wage hikes have increased the salaries paid and caused labor costs to inch up. Universities and colleges are having to change the way jobs have been done in the past.

Shortages of Labor

Managers of B&Is, hospitals, and prisons say that shortages of skilled labor constitute their biggest problem today. These shortages can be expected to influence the future quality of food, the degree of creativity in the foodservice/restaurant industry , and how much preparation will be done in individual kitchens.

Increases in Asians and Hispanics in the Job Market

The increases in Asians and Hispanics in the service industry will have an impact on the industry's way of operating. There will be a greater need for English as a second language training. The language problems will influence such things as recipe directions, use of convenience foods to avoid the need for reading recipes, dials on ovens, and safety features on equipment.

INCREASING COSTS OF LABOR

Competition for labor will increase salaries and fringe benefits offered and the hike in minimum wage rates. This increase in labor costs will be causing management to put more emphasis on increasing productivity, reducing needs for people by using automation, serving convenience food, and by utilizing centralized preparation (commissary-type), and simplifying and standardizing operations.

INCREASES IN PRIVATIZATION

Increases in privatization are occurring for a number of reasons, such as:

- Shortage of trained directors to replace retirees

- Pressure of institutional-type foodservices to operate more like businesses

- Buying power of large management companies

- Need to reduce labor costs

- Need for the capital outlay by large management companies to renovate the facilities

Some segments of the industry have been more inclined to go to privatization, as can be seen when comparing the data. For example, in 1993 only 69 percent of the B&I accounts were contracted, whereas today

90 percent of the business and industry foodservice operations are operated by management companies--and labor costs and the lack of sufficient buying power are probably the two main reasons. For example, the employees at a self-operated B&Is might earn $10-$12 per hour, whereas a contractor's personnel are being paid $6-$7 per hour.

With low unemployment rates in 1998 in the United States, even McDonald's is paying students over $7 per hour to obtain the needed labor. Full-time employees are shopping around, and the entry level pay in some parts of the country is between $9 and $11 per hour without benefits figured into the costs.

The National Association of College and University Food Services reports that as of June 1997, 24 percent of the colleges and universities have contract-management. This is likely to increase because self-operated colleges have the highest board rates, mainly because of labor costs. The need for capital outlay for renovating has been behind many successfully operated university foodservices going to a contractor, e.g., the University of Tennessee. In the past many self-operated universities/colleges have been very strong with excellent, innovative management in some of the larger schools, e.g., the University of Maryland, the University of Georgia, and Penn State.

Only about 8 percent of the public schools' foodservices are contracted out to management companies; however, this will change drastically within the next five years. The management companies are making some inroads as they take over the top ten largest school districts, including Houston (TX) and Chicago (IL). The threat of privatization in the 1990s has had a major influence on how the self-operated directors and staff are managing school foodservices, making it harder for management companies to get into some of the school districts.

Correctional institutions/prisons are also being slow to turn to contractors--about 15 percent. On the other hand, health care management has turned between 35 and 45 percent of the health care foodservices over to contractors during the late 1990s. Again the influence of the threat of privatization has been seen in all the industries as managers of self-operated foodservices are motivated to operate like businesses.

Management companies are doing some positive and innovative things in the industry. They have the accounting systems and the computerization to make it possible to study the data and know where to improve foodservice operations. The use of computers to increase productivity has just begun. This all makes the management companies more appealing, as they can do the job for less. For example, Marriott Management Services has set itself up as very competitive, with its full distribution systems providing the food and supplies at lower prices than its competitors can obtain--as much as a 17 percent savings on procurement.

Increasing Competition

There is probably no area with as much competition as the foodservice industry. Burger King and Wendy's will continue competing with McDonald's for the fast-food business. Supermarkets, convenience stores, and service stations are vying for the food dollar. Syscos, Krafts, and Allied Foods are competing to be the prime distributor for the foodservice industry's needs. Management companies are competing for the self-operated foodservice industry.

The pressure of the competition on management has brought the stress levels up.

CHANGING DEMANDS

Customers Demanding More

No trend is more obvious than customers demanding more value. Another trend (and demand) that will continue is for healthier foods and more nutritional information on foods they eat. The customer is wanting to know how many calories are eaten and how much "hidden" fats are in foods.

Varied portion sizes will be needed as the customers refuse to throw away good food and desire "good buys."

Food Safety Awareness

Recent food poisoning outbreaks have prompted the foodservice industry to be more conscious of bacteria, how bacteria grow, and the need to be extra careful. The health departments and sanitarians are increasing the standards of sanitation in their requirements. This is a trend that will have influences over preparation techniques, food costs, and services. In the future, a few cases of food poisoning in the home meal alternatives (HMR) will receive national attention and slow the HMR business temporarily, unless stricter food safety standards are put into place.

INCREASING USE OF COMMISSARIES

The increased use of commissaries started in the 1990s and will continue, as we see the increased demands to reduce labor costs and to standardize products, and the shortages of employees, particularly trained personnel. There will be a demand for more *Sous Vide* (preparation of food) for restaurants, hospitals, and nursing homes, and cook/chill or cook/freeze of some products across the industry.

PURCHASING CHANGES

Electronic commerce will bring about the greatest change in the purchasing process. The competition among distributors will be to the customer's advantage. Small businesses will have better prices at their fingertips with the use of the internet.

Some purchasing changes and trends that will affect costs are:

- Customer demands for greater varieties of foods

- Use of Internet shopping

- A global market

- Higher skill levels required of purchasers

- Paperless purchasing functions

- Fewer companies to provide services

- Distributors reducing their costs of doing business and developing delivery systems to protect their competitiveness

- Cutting out of the "middle man" in purchasing (more purchasing directly from factories), which works for some larger universities and colleges, schools, and chain restaurants

Paperless purchasing functions are taking place today among the larger operations. These functions will soon catch on even in the small operations. With computer-to-computer communication of purchase orders directly from the person ordering to the distributor, the process will require far less lead time and encourage less inventory on the shelves. This was discussed further under electronic commerce in Chapter 7.

More changes have taken place in all segments of the foodservice industry in the last decade than in the previous three decades, and judging from the trends, there are more changes to come.

OTHER INFLUENCES

Maturing American Taste

According to Peter Romeo, editor of *Restaurant Business* magazine, "American taste for fast food has plateaued." The maturing America taste or changes in Americans' food taste toward spicier foods and more variety is part of the reason. Rich sauces are being replaced by more natural foods, lightly sauteed.

Technology, Computerization, and Automation

Technology, computerization, and automation are finally making progress in the foodservice industry, mainly because of the following:

- Hardware and software friendlier and less expensive

- Outside influences urging more use of computerization, e.g., food distributors requesting that orders be placed by modem

- Moneyless society trends--use of smart cards or credit and debit cards

- Need to increase productivity

- Improvements in vending machines

- Customers' demand for service when and where they want it, fostering the return of the automat and an increased use of vending machines

This subject was discussed in more detail in Chapter 7 of this text.

GLOSSARY OF TERMS

Accounting period--The period of time in which the income and expenses are being analyzed, e.g., daily, weekly, or monthly.

Accounting system--System of measuring, communicating, and interpreting of financial activity.

Accounts payable--The amounts for goods or services received that are owed by the foodservice operation or company for foods and services.

Accounts receivable--The amounts billed for services rendered but not received by the foodservice operation.

Accrual accounting--An accounting system in which revenue is recorded when earned, even though not collected, and expenses when incurred, even though not paid yet.

Actual pricing method--Setting the selling price based on the actual cost of food and direct labor involved.

Administrative costs--Upper management, supervision, technical support, corporate expenses such as accounting, payroll, purchasing, legal costs. Usually a fixed amount.

Allowable fund balance--A phrase that is used in public schools referring to a federal regulation that limits a school district's net cash resources or fund balance. The limitation is to an amount that does not exceed three months of operation.

Appropriation--The budgetary authority to expend funds.

Asset--Value of items owned by the foodservice operation or company.

Attendance factor--A phrase that applies to schools referring to the average number of students present at the school on a given day.

Audit--A system used to evaluate an operation's financial accounting to determine if it is in compliance with laws and regulations.

Audit trail--A procedure that can be used to trace through all stages of an accounting system to verify that the revenue is correct and has been correctly expended (includes support documents).

B&I--Business and industry.

Balance sheet-- A "snapshot" of an operation's financial status--a statement that shows assets and liabilities and fund balance--as of a given day.

Bank reconciliation--The process of matching the monthly bank statement with the deposits and checks written.

Baseline budget--A budget based on the assumption that all the previous year's expenditures were necessary and will be duplicated and that the projected revenue will not change.

Base-price method--Method of setting the selling price first then determining how much is available to spend on food.

Beginning inventory--The dollar value of the products on hand at the beginning of the accounting period; the ending inventory of one accounting period becomes the beginning inventory for the next accounting period.

Bid--Formalized financial (and/or operating) proposal for a given service(s) or product(s).

Blind receiving--Receiving a delivery, checking in the delivery without the quantities on the delivery ticket, and filling in quantities on the delivery ticket as the order is checked in.

Bottom-up budget--A decentralized approach to budget planning whereby each cost center plans a budget and the operation's overall budget is made up by combining all the cost centers' budgets together.

Break-even point (BEP)--The amount of revenue needed to cover all costs--the fixed and variable costs.

Budget--An organized financial plan for a specified period of time (usually a year) that projects sales or revenue and expenses.

Capital budget--Expenses for major pieces of equipment and facilities that will continue over several years.

Cash accounting--A system whereby revenues are recorded when received and expenses when paid--e.g., bank account.

Cash over or cash short--Failure to reconcile cash and charge sales to point-of-sale register tapes.

Central kitchen--A kitchen or facility that prepares menu items or meals for delivery to other sites.

Check average--Dollar sales divided by the number of people served.

Commodities--Donated foods provided by the United States Department of Agriculture to school foodservice programs under the National School Lunch Program.

Contract--Legal agreement between two people or groups to provide a given service or product based on specific criteria.

Contribution margin--The percentage of the revenue (the cents out of every dollar) left after the variable cost percent has been subtracted from 100% (representing the dollars in revenue) that can be used to pay the fixed costs.

Controllable cost--Costs, usually variable costs, that can be changed in a short time.

Convenience food preparation--Using a maximum amount of processed or prepared food.

Conventional food preparation--Preparation which is generally from raw ingredients.

Cooperative purchasing--Group purchasing when more than one foodservice operation purchases using competitive bids.

Cost center--Location that incurs costs, e.g., convenience store, dorm's dining services, cafeteria, warehouse, or snack bar.

Cost plus buying--A percentage charged over the cost. The cost may fluctuate based on the market.

Credit--A decrease in assets and an increase in liabilities. (In a general ledger or "T" account, the credit is on the right-hand side of a double-entry posting.)

Credit memo--An addition to a delivery slip that states shortages and differences from what is on the delivery slip.

Cycle menu--Set of menus that repeat, e.g., 7-day cycle.

Debit--An increase in assets and a decrease in liabilities. In a general ledger or "T" account, the debit is on the left-hand side of a double-entry posting.

Deficit--The result when expenditures exceed revenue.

Depreciation--The portion of the original cost of equipment or property that is recorded as an expense during the time the equipment or property is in use.

Direct costs--Costs that do not vary with the day-to-day or week-to-week volumes of sales or numbers of customers served.

Disposables--Single-service items made from paper, plastic, and other products.

Dual pricing--Use of two meal prices, e.g., a high school offering two student lunch prices.

ECR--Electronic cash register that has some memory and can be programmed.

Electronic commerce--Use of computerization/automation to handle various steps involved in purchasing.

Encumbrances--Financial commitments or anticipated expenditures, e.g., purchase orders, contracts, salaries, and other commitments, which are canceled when paid.

Ending inventory--Dollar amounts of foods and supplies on hand at the end of the accounting period.

Enterprise fund--A fund in a nonprofit setting that is expected to generate revenue from the sale of goods and services and is treated as a business, e.g., school foodservice in a public school setting (sometimes referred to as proprietary or revolving funds).

Equity, owner's--The owner's claims to assets.

Equivalent meal--A common measurement of work involved in foodservices (includes equating work involved in producing and serving breakfast, lunch, dinner, snacks, and a la carte sales).

Expenditures--Funds spent for goods and services, including labor costs and fringe benefits.

FIFO--Process of "first in first out," or rotating of inventory or stock.

Finishing kitchen--A kitchen that receives food partially prepared somewhere else and finishes the preparation of the food and serves it.

Franchise fee--Fee paid for the right to do business in a specific way, use of the company name, the recipes, and gains from advertising done by the franchisers, e.g., Pizza Hut, Subway, Starbuck.

Gross pay--Employee salary before deductions.

Gross profit or gross margin--The revenue after costs of goods (food) have been deducted.

Fiscal year--A period of one year, the beginning and the ending dates of which are set by the operation. (It may be the same as the calendar year, the government year [October 1 through September 30], or the school year [usually July 1 through June 30].)

Fixed costs--Costs that are not affected by changes in sales (remain relatively constant or the same during a given period of time regardless of the number served).

Foodservice management company--A commercial enterprise or nonprofit organization that manages the foodservice operation under contract for a fee.

Forecasting--Projecting of quantities or events, e.g., future sales or expenses (used in the process of production and in estimating quantities of food needed in advance for placing orders).

FTE-Full-time equivalent employee; made up of part-time employee hours.

General ledger--A part of accounting that contains accounts, assets, liabilities, fund balances, revenues, and expenditures.

Gross margin or gross profit--Profit after deducting costs of food and supplies and costs of labor necessary for producing the services from the total revenue.

Income--Revenue less expenses.

Income statement--Profit and loss statement, or statement of operation; a financial report that contains the revenue taken in for a period of time less the expenditures during the same period of time with the difference being a profit or a loss (also known as P&L statement and Statement of Income).

Indirect cost--Cost generally associated with the occupancy of a facility--space in building, utilities, property taxes, maintenance--and administrative costs, such as purchasing and payroll and other administrative support.

Inventory--A list of each item in storage at a given time along with the quantities.

Inventory turnover--Measurement of the effective use of capital, by determining through calculation the average inventory for a period of time based on costs of food used for the same period.

Invoice--An itemized statement to the purchaser of charges for goods or services rendered.

Liability--What is owed by the operation (obligations).

LIFO--The practice of using the "last-in stock as first-out."

Management fees--Direct operating expenses in a client/contractor relationship where foodservices are managed on a fee-for-service basis. The cost is usually based on a percentage of sales or a fixed fee, but would vary in relationship to volume of sales. It includes profit and corporate overhead charges.

Management information system (MIS)--A system of collecting, storing, and disseminating data.

Market value--The cost when purchased.

Meals per labor hour (MPLH)--Commonly used to measure productivity rate of employees.

Modified accrual--System of accounting adapted to governmental funds--not recommended for foodservices. (The revenues are recognized when they become "measurable"; however, all expenditures may not be recognized [recorded] even though they have been incurred.)

Net cash--All monies that are available at a given time, less cash payable. (Such monies may include, but are not limited to, cash on hand, cash receivable, earnings on investments, cash on deposit, and the value of stocks, bonds, or other negotiable securities.)

Net profit--The revenue left after all expenses and taxes have been paid.

Net sales--The revenue left after taxes.

Nonprofit--Classified as exempt from income tax under Section 501 (c)(3) of the Internal Revenue Code of 1954.

Non-voluntary fringe benefit costs--Required fringe benefits, such as FICA, workmen's compensation, Medicare, and unemployment insurance.

Offer versus serve--Term that applies to school foodservices operating under meeting the requirements of National School Lunch and Child Nutrition programs for reimbursable meals. (The regulation states that children must be offered a complete meal for the meal to qualify for federal subsidy, but children may select less, e.g., three of the five items under the School Lunch Pattern.)

PAR stock--A certain level of stock maintained that requires reordering once the inventory goes below that level.

Perpetual inventory--An inventory system that is a continuous record (count) on each item in stock or on hand.

Physical inventory--A physical count of each item in stock at the end of the accounting period (end of month) or prior to placing orders.

Point of sale (POS)--Terminals for accounting for sales located at the exit of a restaurant or at the end of a serving line--usually refers to computerized cash registers.

Point of service--For schools, the point in the foodservice operation where meals are served and payments are collected.

Portion-pak--A pack containing a preportioned, individual serving, usually condiments such as jelly and sugar.

Postcosting--The process of determining the actual cost of a recipe, a portion, a menu item, or a meal after it has been prepared and served.

Precosting--The process of determining the cost of a recipe, a portion, a menu item, or a meal prior to preparation or service.

Prime costs--The food and labor costs that make up the greatest percentages of expenses.

Processing contracts--Agreements between companies and school districts or state departments of education for the company to turn donated commodities into finished products, such as whole chickens into chicken nuggets.

Proportioned--Being in serving sizes.

Production record--Record of forecasted quantities, total quantity of food produced, portion sizes, actual quantity used, number served, and amount left over.

Production schedule--A schedule of foods to be prepared with the time and specific quantities that are to be produced.

Productivity rate--Ratio of measurement of labor's efficiency. (Divide the output by the input and the result is the productivity rate.)

Productivity standard--Measurement of effectiveness of staff that is considered the acceptable productivity rate.

Profit--The revenue that exceeds expenditures.

Profit and loss statement--(See income statement or statement of income.)

Proprietary funds--Enterprise funds. Funds charged for services.

Purchase order--A document issued to a vendor that authorizes the delivery of specified merchandise or services.

Ratio analysis--The comparison of figures.

Receiving kitchen--The foodservice location that receives food ready to serve.

Requisition--A document submitted initiating a purchase order to purchase services or goods.

Revenue--The income or sales.

Sales history--A record of numbers served by category and day/date.

Sales mix--Process of analyzing what menu items make up the sales.

Satellite foodservice--System whereby food is prepared in one location and transported to other locations to be served.

Severe-need breakfast school--A school that served 40 percent or more of the lunches free or at reduced price in the second preceding school year and can receive additional federal subsidies for each free or reduced-price breakfast meal served.

Severe-need lunch school district--A school district that served 60 percent or more of the lunches free or at a reduced price in the second preceding year and is reimbursed for meals at a higher rate (in 1999 school year it was two cents).

Shortfall or slippage--A negative variance of actual performance from what was planned or budgeted.

Shrinkage-The difference between what should be in inventory and what is in inventory.

Sous Vide--The system where food is prepared and stored in a plastic pouch that withstands extremely high and low temperatures. (The food is cooked at a low temperature, cooled quickly, then stored for later use.)

Statement of income--(See income statement.)

Subsidy--Monetary and other assistance provided a foodservice operation (e.g., rent-free space provided by business and industry and no charges for utilities and custodial services provided to keep the prices to employees lower and encourage employees to utilize the in-house foodservices in lieu of employees taking an extended off-site lunch).

Table d' hote--A complete meal at one price. (The menu is set by the planner and may be limited in choice.)

Top-down budget--A centralized budget planned for more than one cost center.

Turnover rate--The ratio of employees who have left employment in comparison with those on the workforce. (The number of separations is divided by the average number of employees for the period of time equal the turnover rate.)

Uniform system of accounts--A standardized system of accounting for different segments of the foodservice industry. (There are several different ones for the different segments of the industry.)

USDA--United States Department of Agriculture.

Variable costs--Costs affected by sales that vary in direct proportion to volume of sales or number of customers served, e.g., food and disposable products used vary as volume varies.

Variance analysis--The process of determining differences between planned and actual.

Voluntary fringe benefit costs--Fringe benefits beyond those required, such as health insurance, retirement, IRA, stock options, and life insurance.

Walk--A check unpaid by a customer.

Weighted average--The average of different components that make up the whole.

Work simplification--The process of finding the easiest and most efficient way of doing a job.

Zero-based budget--A budget planned as if for the first time by determining revenue and expenditures in detail.

BIBLIOGRAPHY

American Hotel and Motel Association. 1987. *Uniform System of Accounts and Expense Dictionary for Small Hotels and Motels*, 14th ed. East Lansing, MI: Educational Institute of the American Hotel and Motel Association.

Bakos, J. B., and G. E. Karrick. 1989. *Handbook of Noncommercial Foodservice Management: Dining in Corporate America.* Rockville, MD: Aspen Publishers, Inc.

Bangs, D. H., Jr. 1992. *Financial Troubleshooting.* Dover, NH: Upstart Publishing Company, Inc.

Barfield, J. T., C. Raiborn, and M. R. Kinney. 1994. *Student Solutions Manual to Accompany Cost Accounting Traditions and Innovations.* 2d ed. Minneapolis, MN: West Publishing Company.

Bernstein, C., and R. Paul. 1994. *Winning the Chain Restaurant Game: 8 Key Strategies.* New York: John Wiley & Sons, Inc.

Byers, B., C. Shanklin, and L. Hoover. 1994. *Food Service Manual for Health Care Institutions.* 1994 ed. Chicago, IL: American Hospital Publishing, Inc.

California Department of Education. 1992. *California School Accounting Manual.* Sacramento, CA: California Department of Education.

Coltman, M. M. 1993. *Hospitality Management Accounting.* 5th ed. New York City, NY: Van Nostrand Reinhold, Inc.

Consumer Metrics. 1994. *Second Annual Benchmarking Study.* Louisville, KY: Society of Foodservice Management.

Cornyn, J., J. Coons-Fasano, and M. Schechter. 1995. *Noncommercial Foodservice: An Administrator's Handbook.* New York City, NY: John Wiley & Sons, Inc.

Dittmer, P. R., and G. G. Griffin. 1989. *Principles of Food, Beverage, & Labor Cost Controls for Hotels and Restaurants.* 4th ed. New York City, NY: Van Nostrand Reinhold, Inc.

The Educational Foundation. 1992. *Basic Accounting for Food Services.* Chicago, IL: National Restaurant Association.

The Educational Foundation. 1992. *Cost Control for Foodservice Managers.* Chicago, IL: National Restaurant Association.

The Educational Foundation. 1992. *Management Accounting for Food Service.* Chicago, IL: National Restaurant Association.

Hess, J. P., and D. VanEgmond-Pannell. 1987. "Budgeting for Food Service Operations." *School Business Affairs* 53 (11): 35-37.

Kaud, F. A., Editor. 1989. *Effective Computer Management in Food and Nutrition Services.* Rockville, MD: Aspen Publishers, Inc.

Keiser, J. 1989. *Controlling and Analyzing Costs in Foodservice Operations.* 3d ed. New York City, NY: MacMillan Publishing Company.

Lane, H.E., and M. van Hartesvelt. 1983. *Essentials of Hospitality Administration.* Reston, VA: Reston Publishing Company, Inc.

Laventhol & Horwath. 1996. *Uniform System of Accounts for Restaurants: Adopted and Recommended by the National Restaurant Association.* 7th ed. Washington, DC: National Restaurant Association.

Levinson, C. 1989. *Food and Beverage Operation: Cost Control and Systems Management.* Englewood Cliffs, NJ: Prentice Hall, Inc.

McCool, A.C., F.A. Smith, and D. L. Tucker. 1994. *Dimensions of Noncommercial Foodservice Management.* New York City, NY: Van Nostrand Reinhold, Inc.

Mayo, C., M. Olsen, and B. Barbee. 1984. "Use of Employee Time Logs for Time Standard Adjustment," *School Food Service Research Review* 8 (1): 42-44.

Miller, J. E., and D. K. Hayes. 1994. *Basic Food and Beverage Cost Control.* New York City, NY: John Wiley & Sons, Inc.

Miller, J. E., and D. V. Pavesic. 1996. *Menu Pricing and Strategy*. 4th ed. New York City, NY: Van Nostrand Reinhold Company.

National Restaurant Association. 1997. *Survey of Wage Rates for Hourly Employees, 1997*. Washington, DC: National Restaurant Association.

National Restaurant Association. 1997. *Restaurant Industry Operations Report*. Washington, DC: National Restaurant Association.

National Restaurant Association. 1996. *Uniform System of Accounts for Restaurants*, 7th ed. Washington, DC: National Restaurant Association.

Ninemeier, J.D. 1995. *Management of Food and Beverage Operations*. 2d ed. East Lansing, MI: The Educational Institute of the American Hotel and Motel Association.

Pannell-Martin, D. 1997. *Cost Control for School Foodservice*. 2d ed. Alexandria, VA: InTEAM Associates, Inc.

Pannell-Martin, D., and G. B. Applebaum. 1995. *InTEAM Food System Administrator's Manual*. Alexandria, VA: InTEAM Associates, Inc.

Pannell-Martin, D., and G. B. Applebaum. 1995. *InTEAM Food System Manager's Manual*. Alexandria, VA: InTEAM Associates, Inc.

Pannell-Martin, D., G.B. Applebaum, and E. Soares. 1998. *Manager's Production Manual*. Alexandria, VA: InTEAM Associates, Inc.

Pappas, M. J. 1996. *Eat Food, Not Profits! How Computers Can Save Your Restaurant*. New York City, NY: Van Nostrand Reinhold, Inc.

Pavesic, D. V. 1998. *Fundamental Principles of Restaurant Cost Control*. Upper Saddle River, NJ: Prentice Hall, Inc.

Sackler, W., and S. Trapani. 1996. *Foodservice Cost Control Using Microsoft Excel for Windows*. New York: John Wiley & Sons, Inc.

Schmidgall, R.S., and J. W. Damitto. 1994. *Hospitality Industry Financial Accounting*. East Lansing, MI: The Educational Institute of the American Hotel and Motel Association.

Sneed, J., and K. H. Dresse. 1989. *Understanding Foodservice Financial Management*. Rockville, MD: Aspen Publishers, Inc..

Society for Foodservice Management. 1994. *Second Annual Benchmarking Study*. Prepared by Consumer Metrics.

Stokes, J. F. 1985. *Cost Effective Quality Food Service: An Institutional Guide*. 2d ed. Rockville, MD: Aspen Publishers, Inc.

VanEgmond-Pannell, D. 1990. *School Foodservice Management*. 4th ed. Alexandria, VA: InTEAM Associates, Inc.

Warner, M. 1989. "Breakeven Analysis and Profit Volume Charting: Function and Use for Restaurant Managers." Presentation at the National Restaurant Association Meeting in Chicago.

INDEX

237